MUSE ABSOLUTION

GUITAR TAB EDITION

 taste *music limited*

 UNIVERSAL MUSIC PUBLISHING GROUP

 naïve

 MUSHROOM

 Café CONCERTO Cafè Concerto Italia S.r.l.

 strictly confidential

 WARNER/CHAPPELL

Exclusive distributors:
Music Sales Limited
8/9 Frith Street, London W1D 3JB, England.
Music Sales Pty Limited
120 Rothschild Avenue, Rosebery, NSW 2018, Australia.

Order No. AM979077
ISBN 1-84449-330-X
This book © Copyright 2003 by
Taste Media Limited.

Music arrangements by Matt Cowe.
Music processed by Paul Ewers Music Design.

Printed in the United Kingdom by
Caligraving Limited, Thetford, Norfolk.

www.musicsales.com

Apocalypse Please

Words by Matthew Bellamy
Music by Matthew Bellamy, Chris Wolstenholme & Dominic Howard

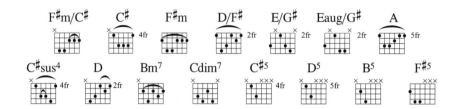

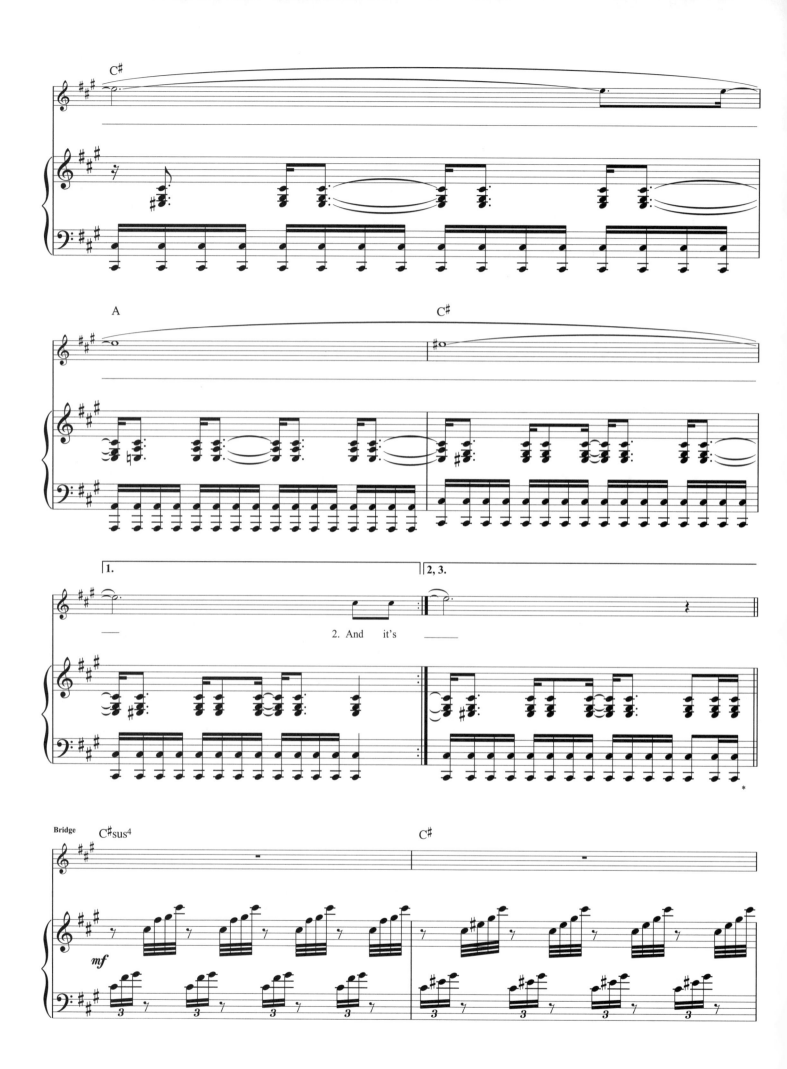

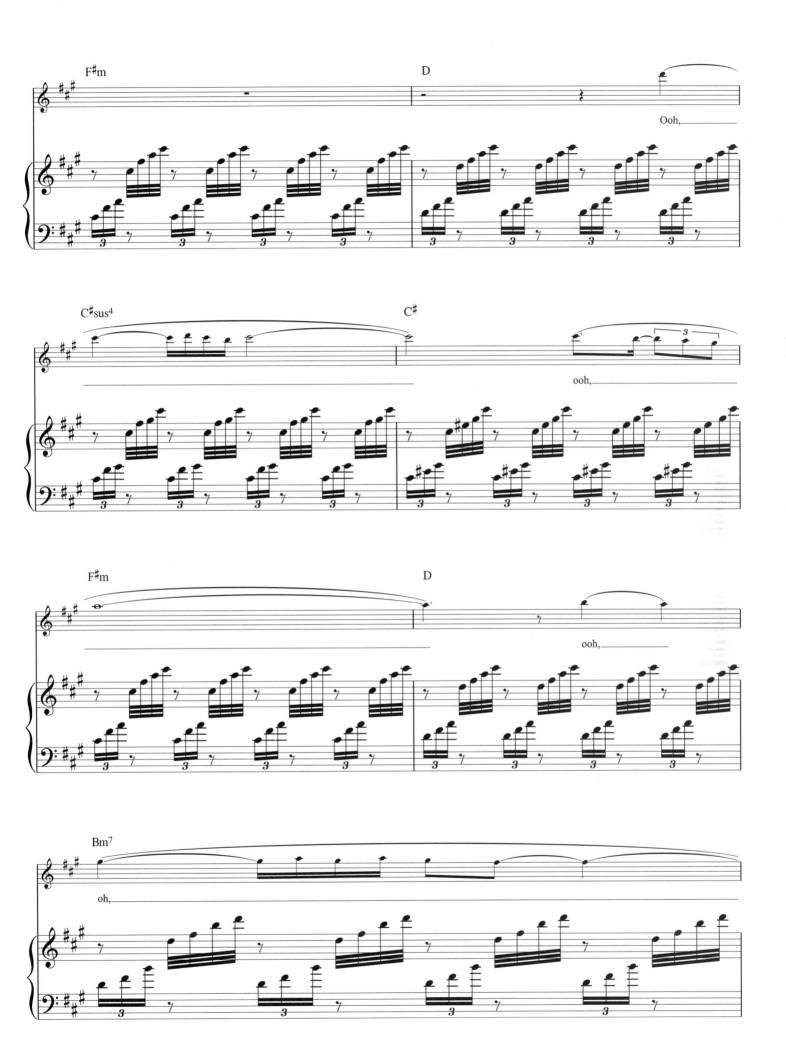

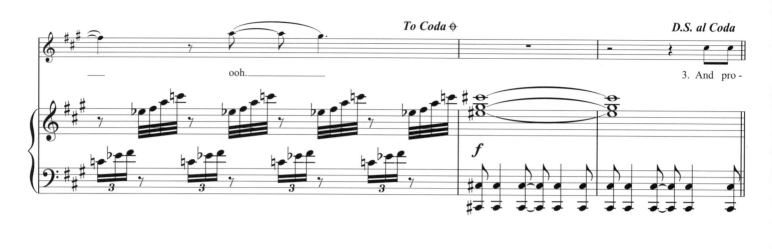

ooh.

To Coda ⊕

D.S. al Coda

3. And pro -

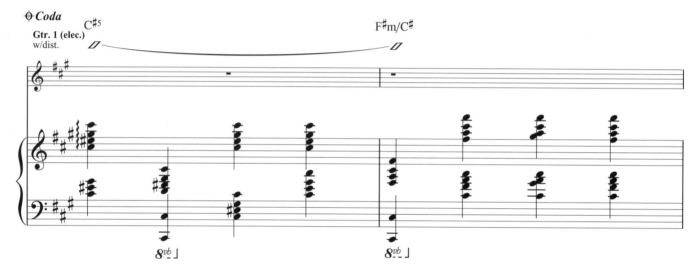

⊕ Coda

Gtr. 1 (elec.)
w/dist.

C#5

F#m/C#

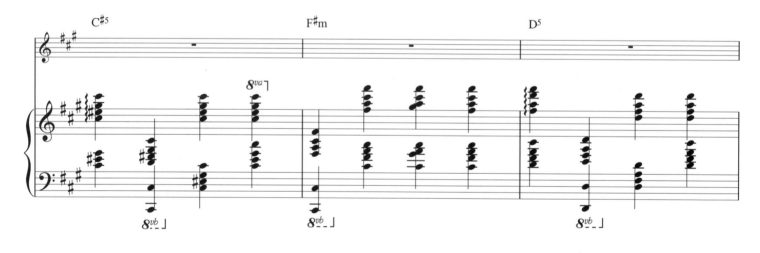

C#5

F#m

D5

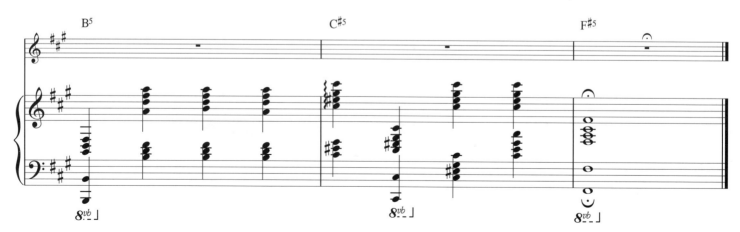

B5

C#5

F#5

Time Is Running Out

Words by Matthew Bellamy

Music by Matthew Bellamy, Chris Wolstenholme & Dominic Howard

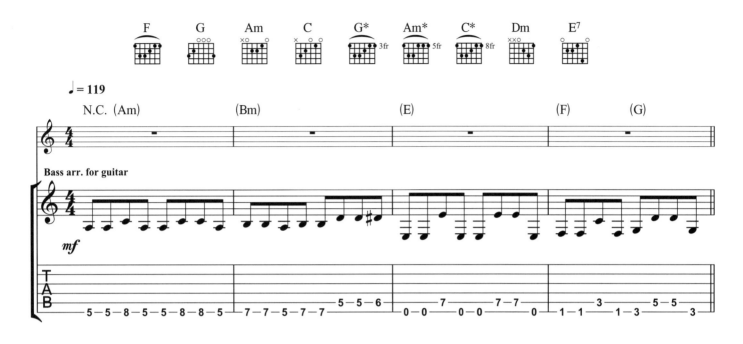

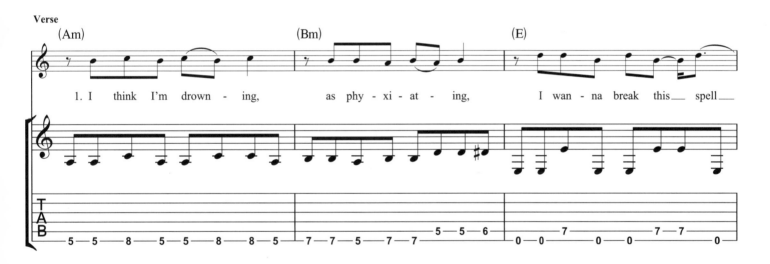

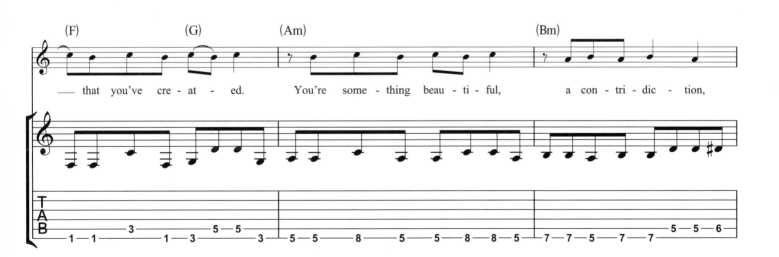

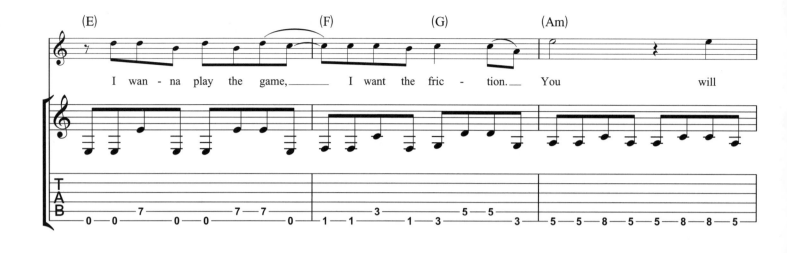

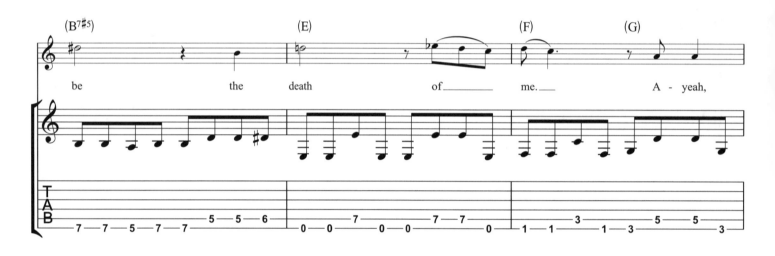

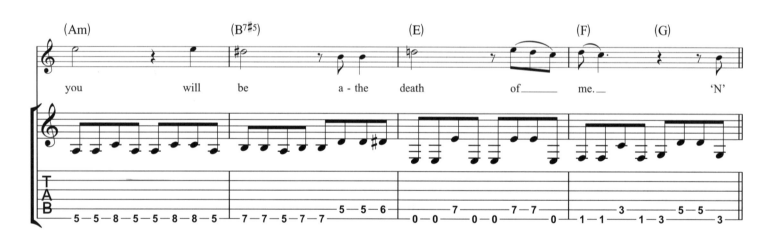

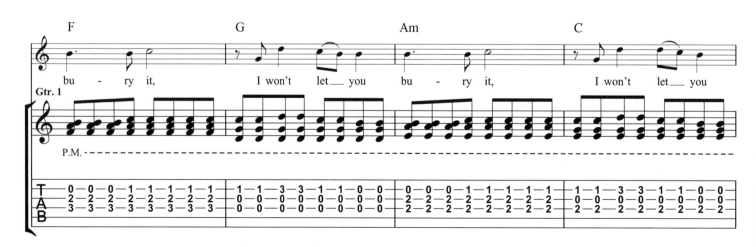

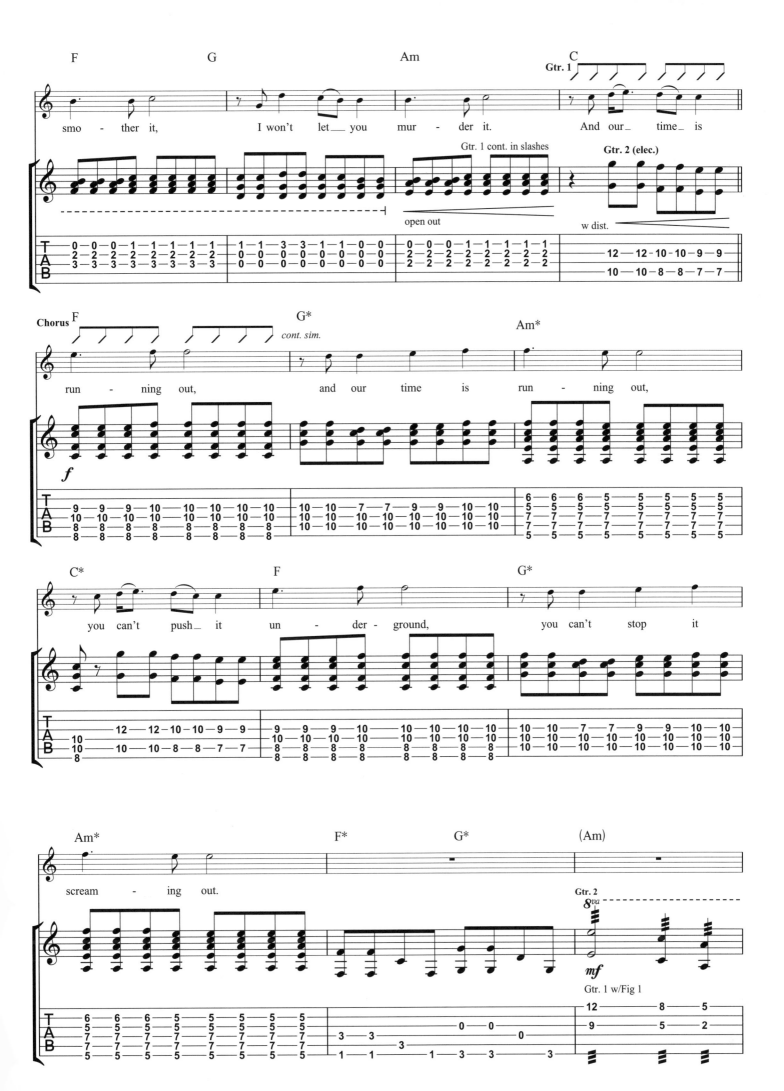

12

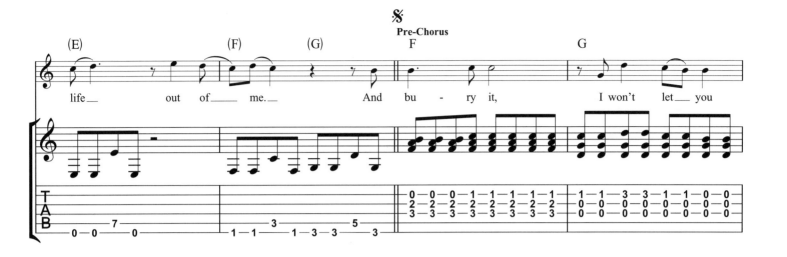

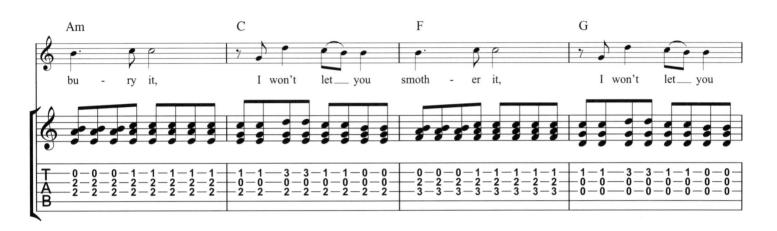

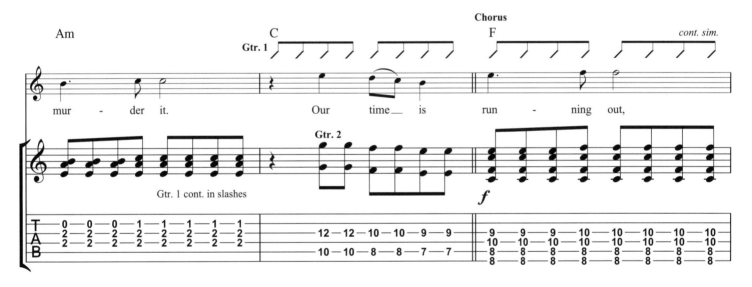

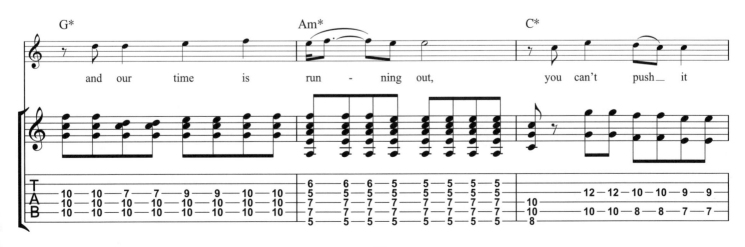

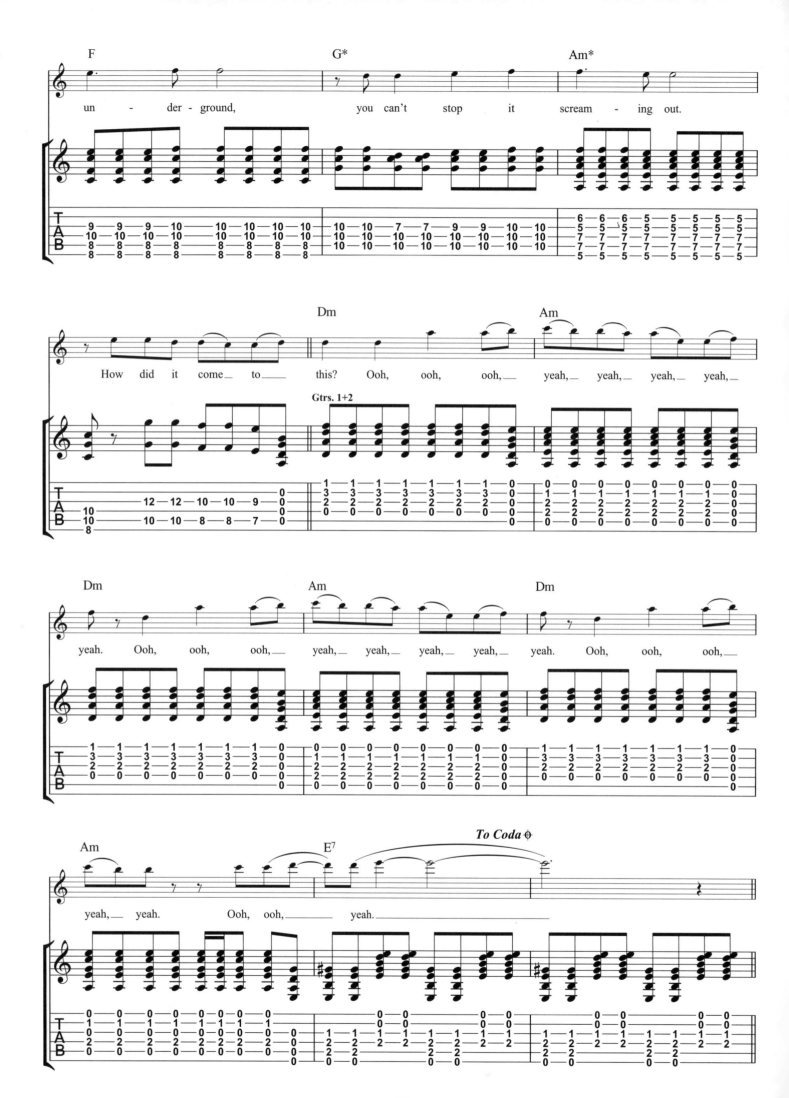

Sing For Absolution

Words by Matthew Bellamy
Music by Matthew Bellamy, Chris Wolstenholme & Dominic Howard

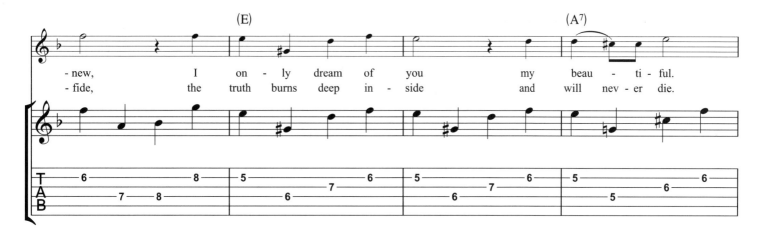

- new, I on - ly dream of you my beau - ti - ful.
- fide, the truth burns deep in - side and will nev - er die.

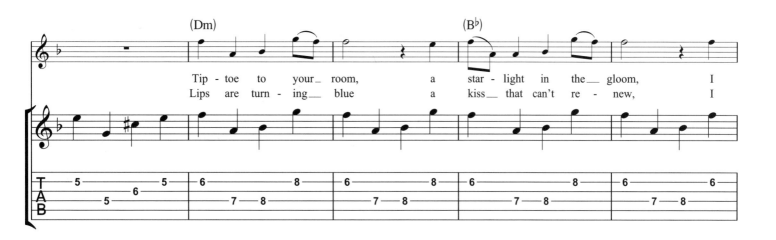

Tip - toe to your room, a star - light in the gloom, I
Lips are turn - ing blue a kiss that can't re - new, I

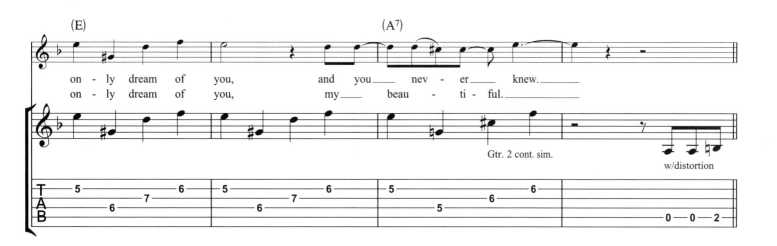

on - ly dream of you, and you nev - er knew.
on - ly dream of you, my beau - ti - ful.

Gtr. 2 cont. sim.

w/distortion

Chorus

harmony 2° only

Sing for ab - so -

Fig. 1 - - - - - - - - - - - - - - -
Gtr. 2 tacet

17

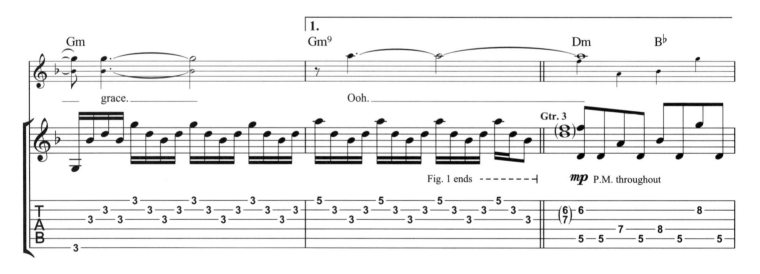

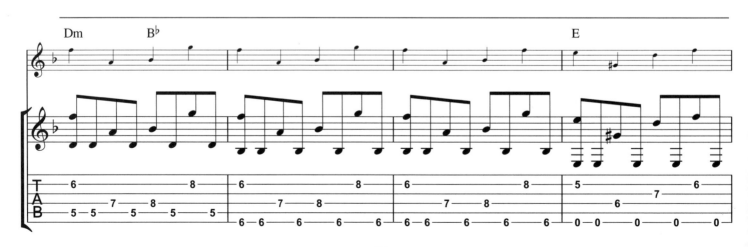

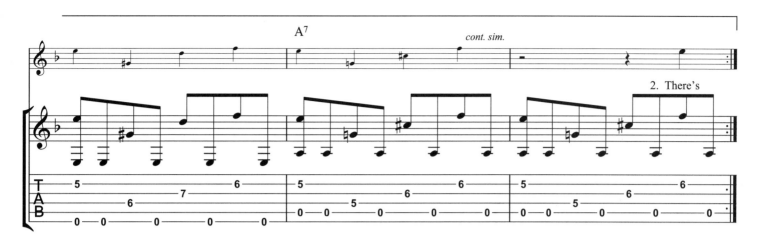

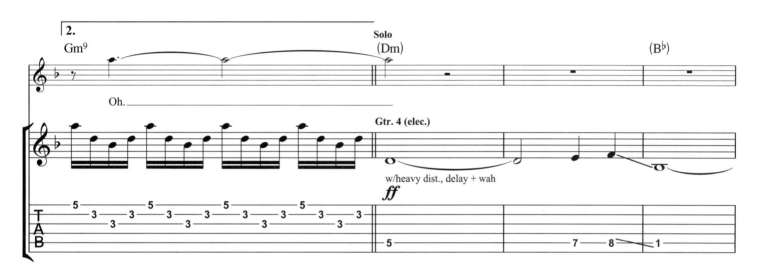

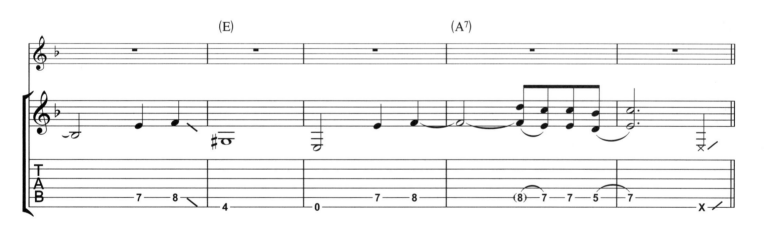

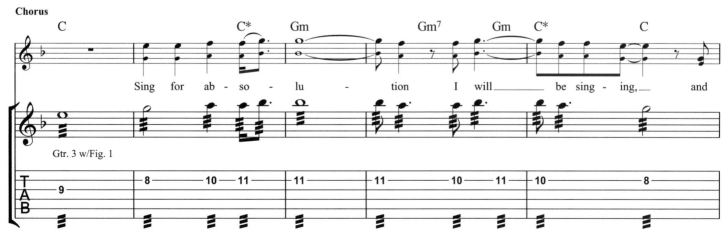

Stockholm Syndrome

Words by Matthew Bellamy
Music by Matthew Bellamy, Chris Wolstenholme & Dominic Howard

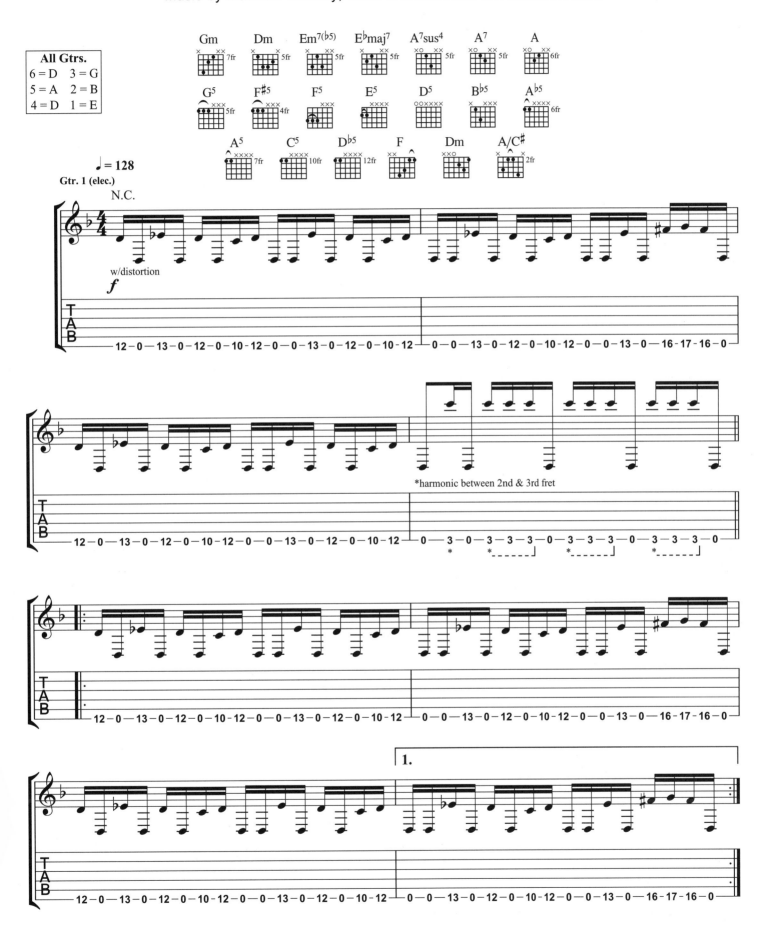

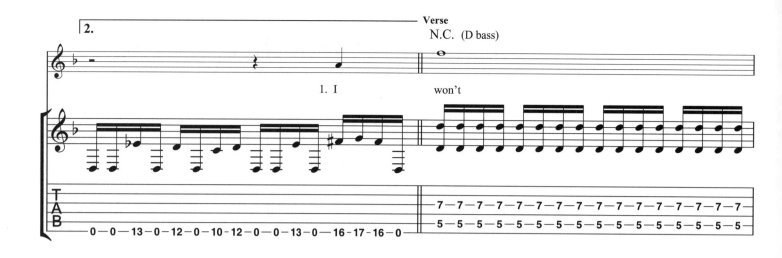

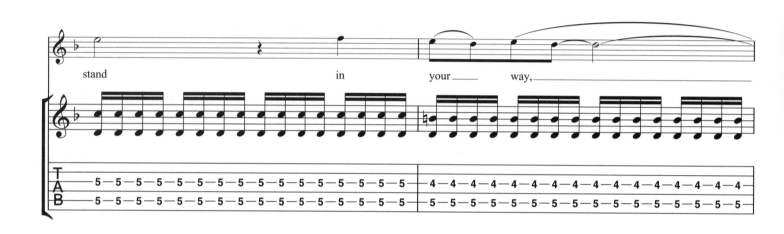

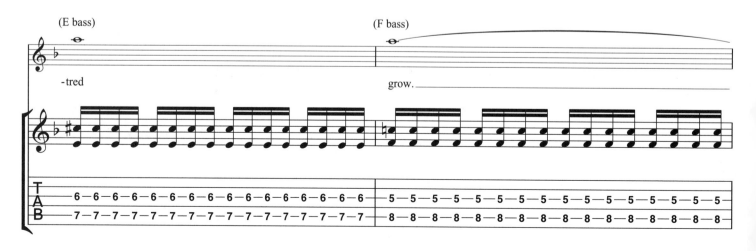

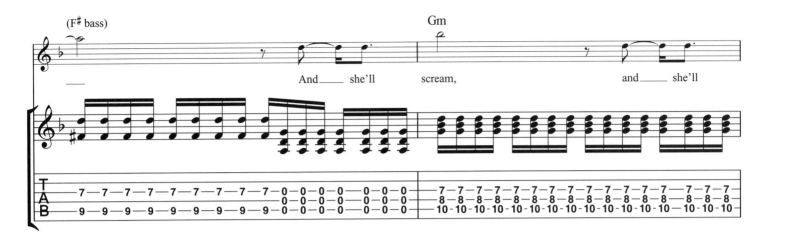

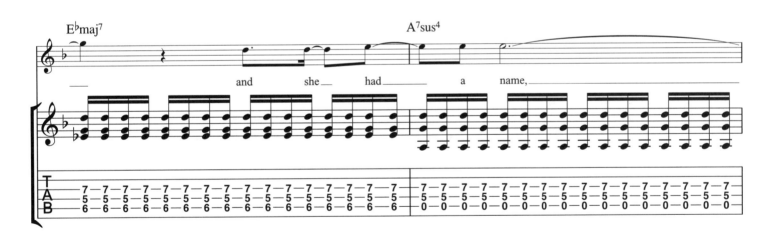

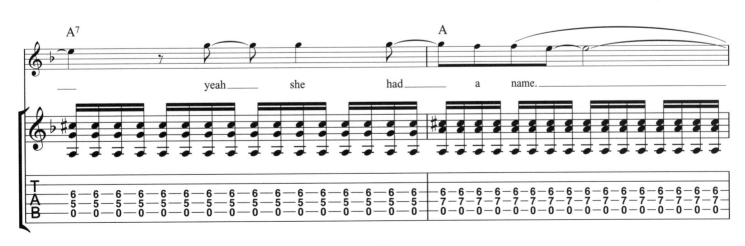

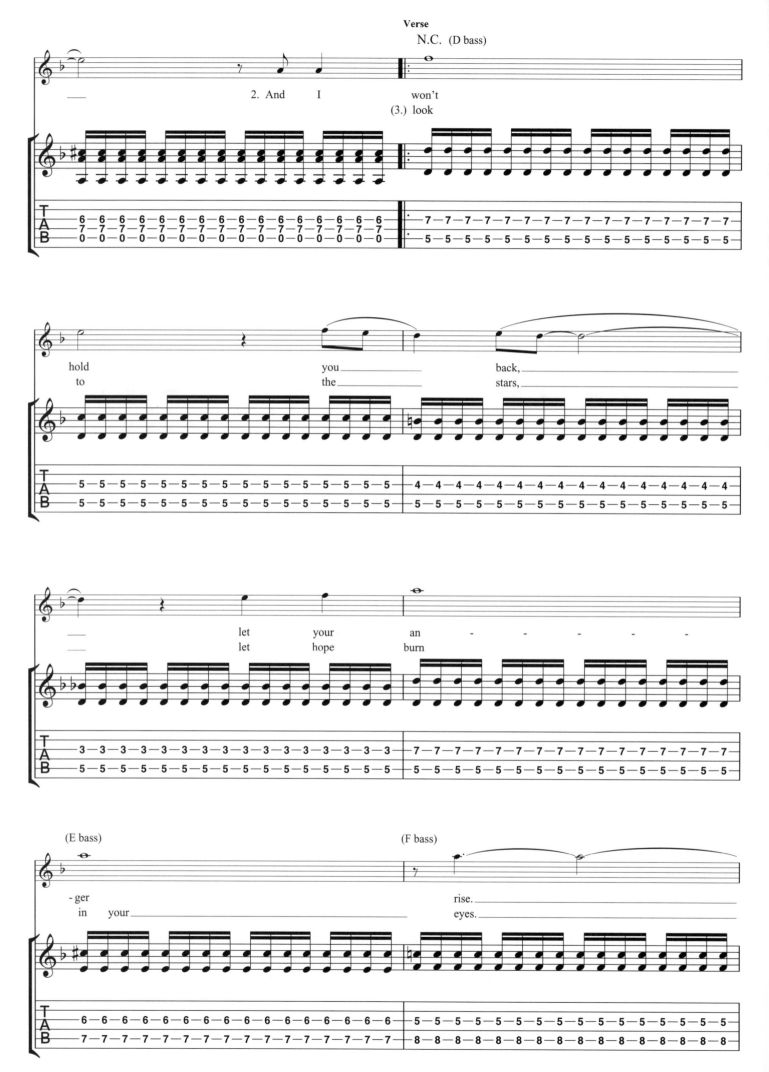

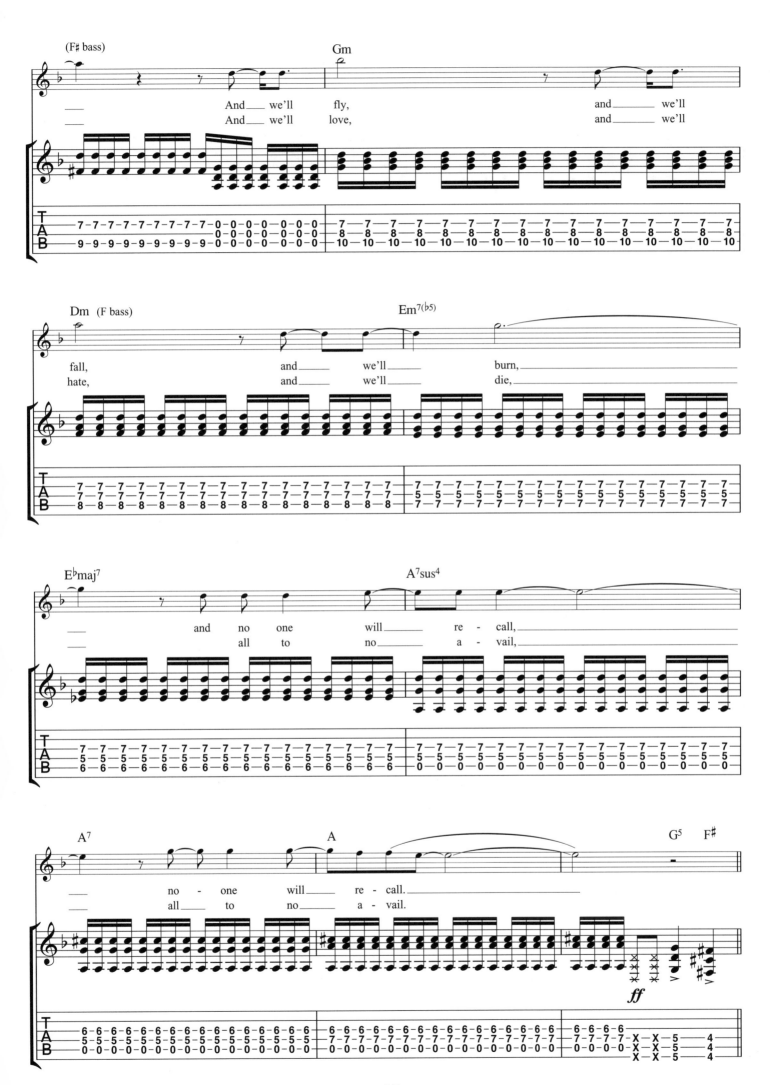

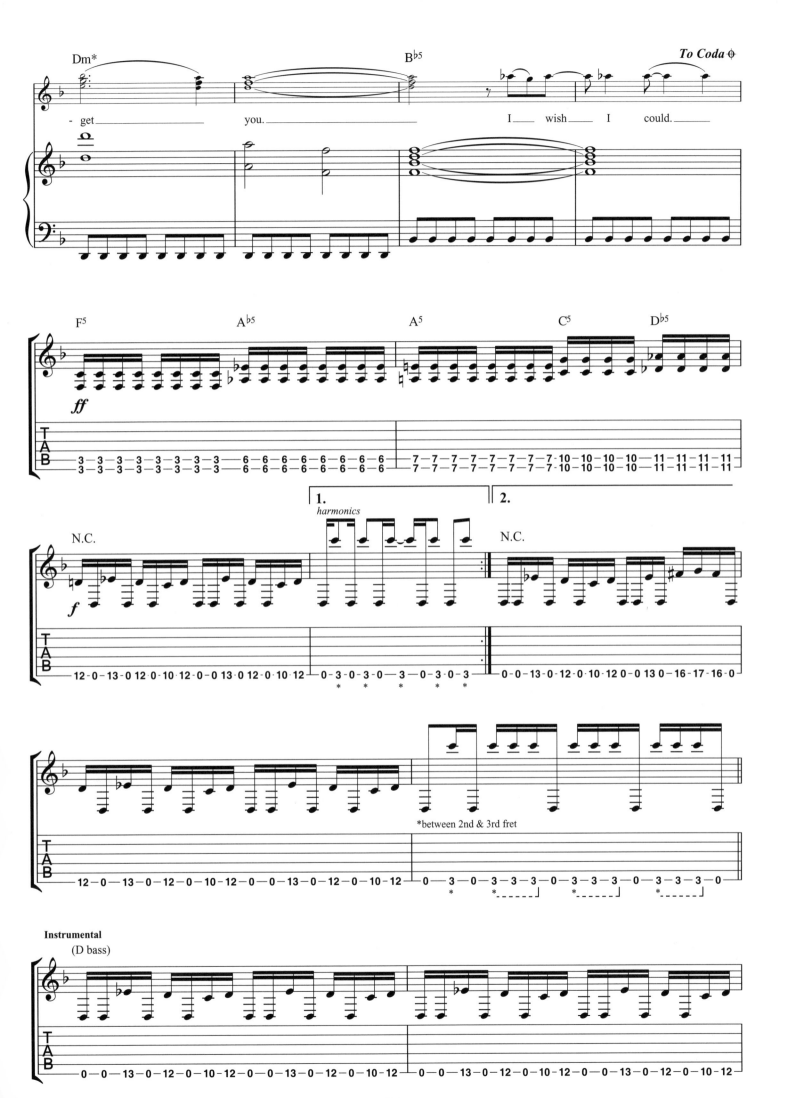

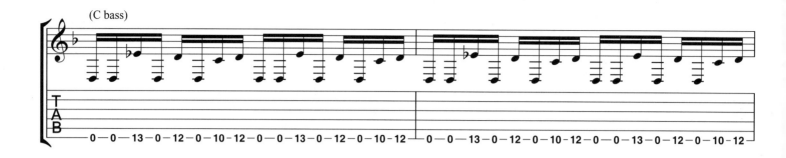

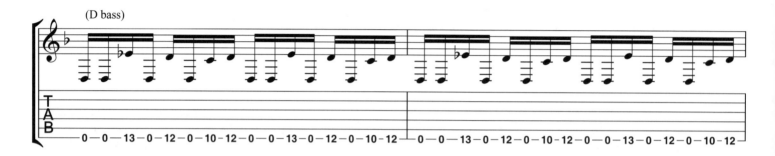

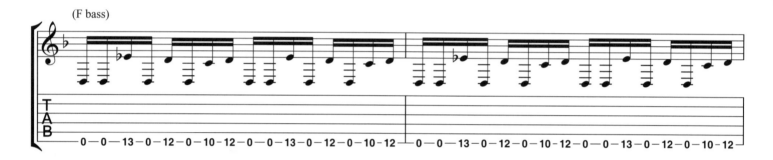

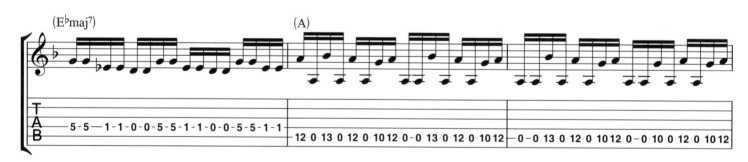

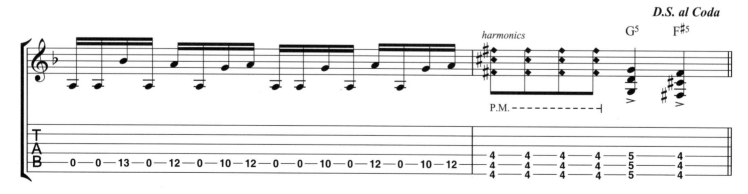

28

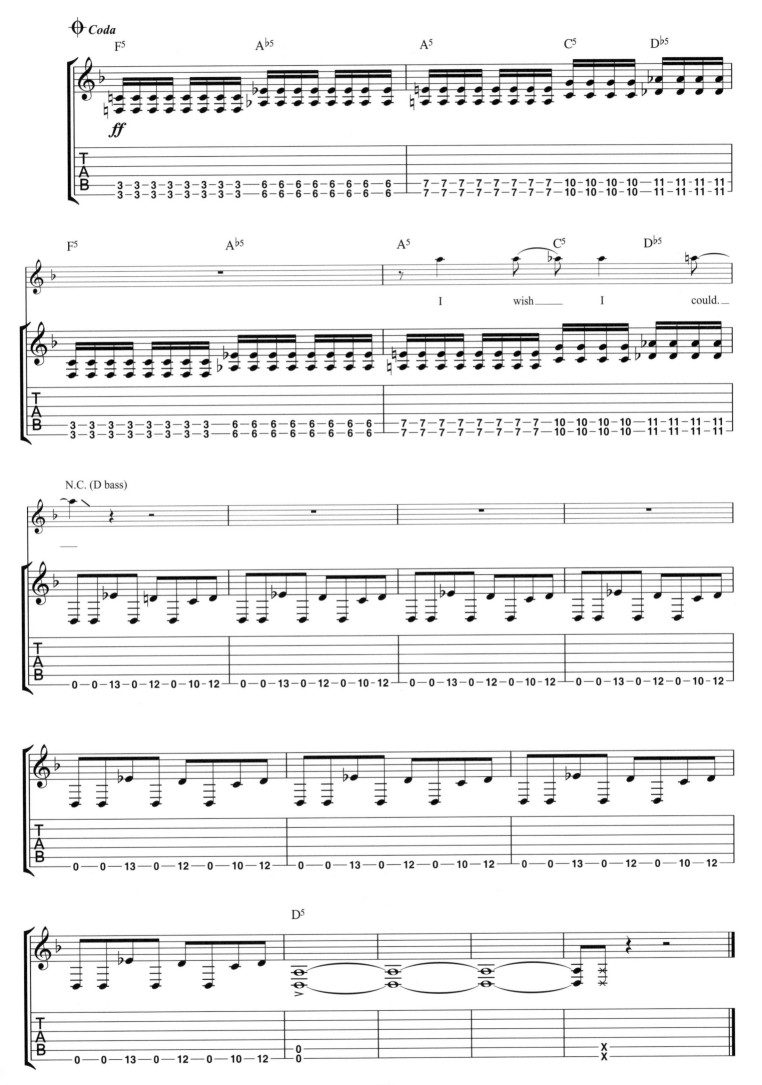

Falling Away With You

Words by Matthew Bellamy
Music by Matthew Bellamy, Chris Wolstenholme & Dominic Howard

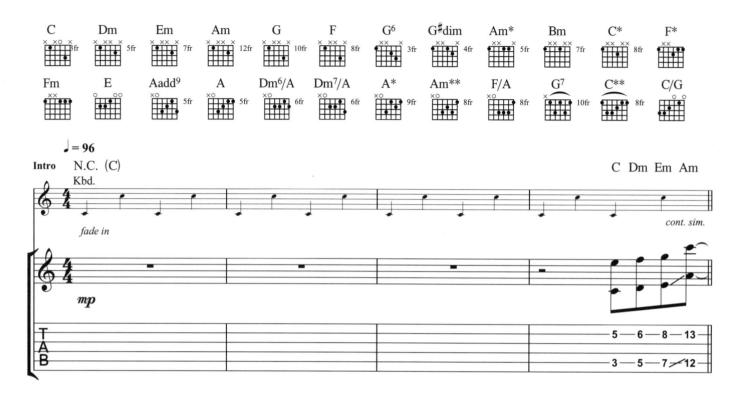

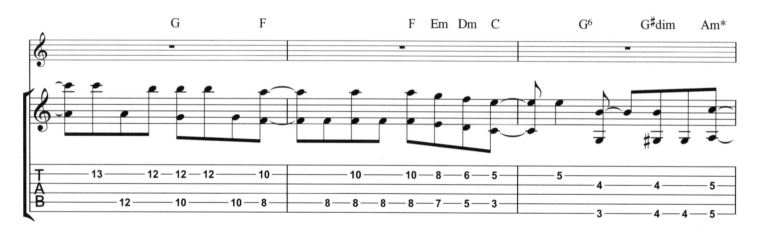

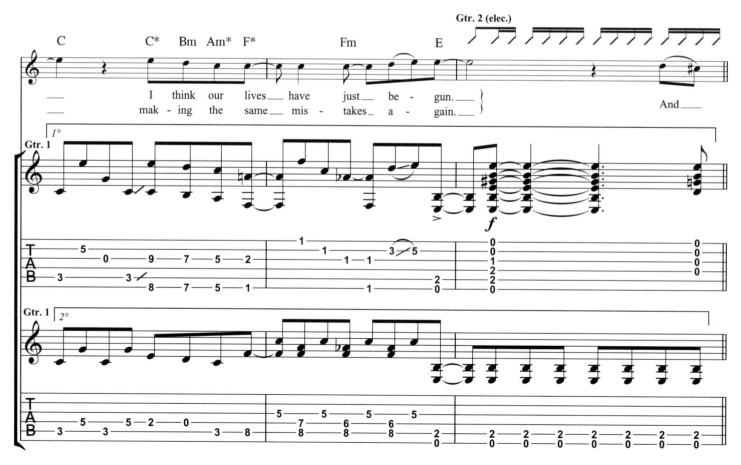

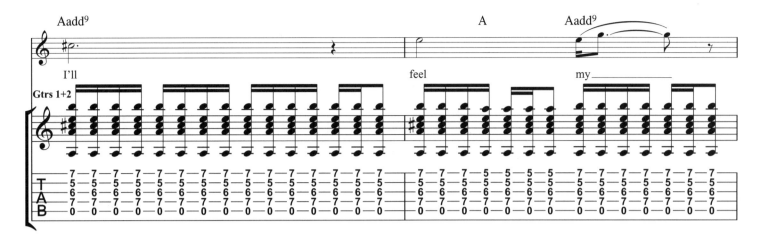

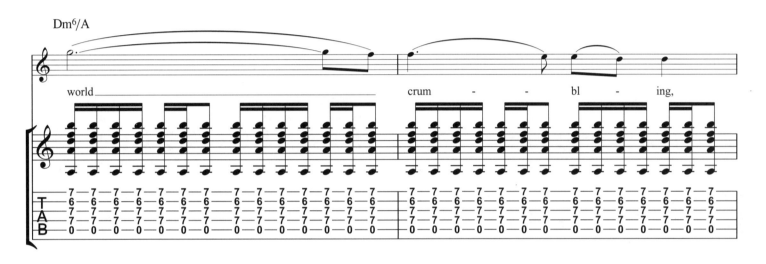

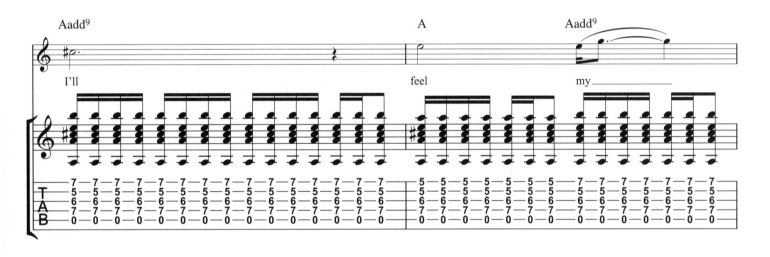

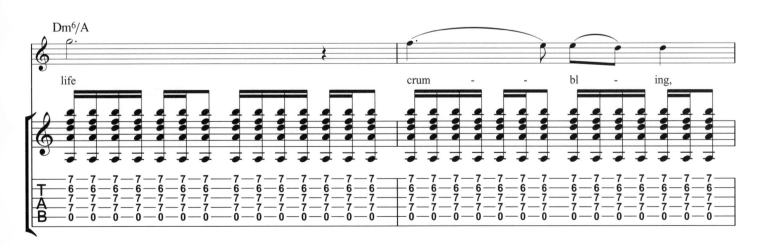

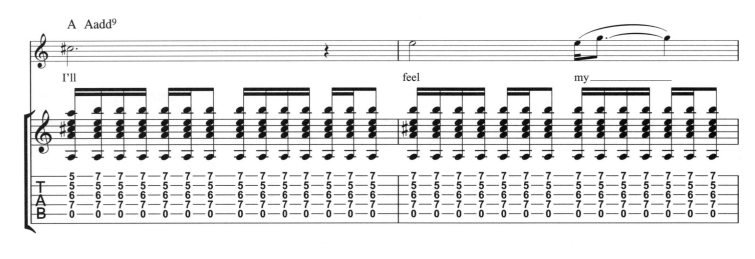

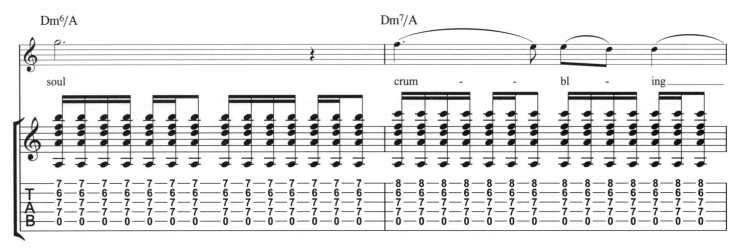

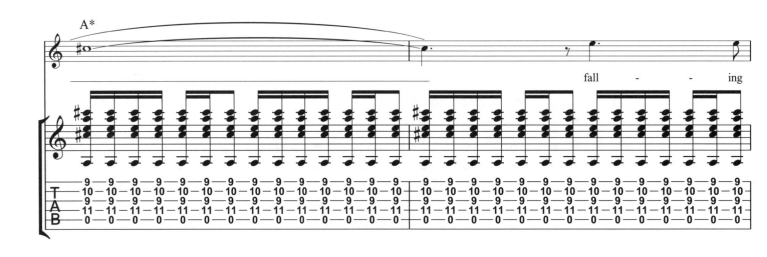

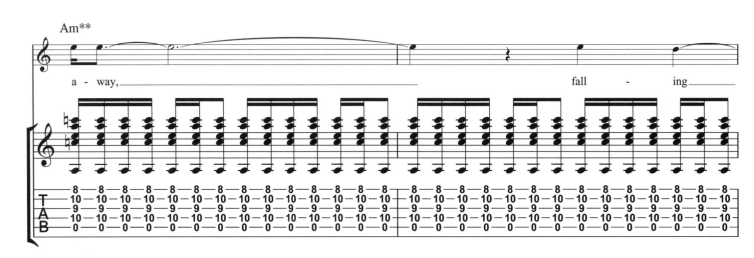

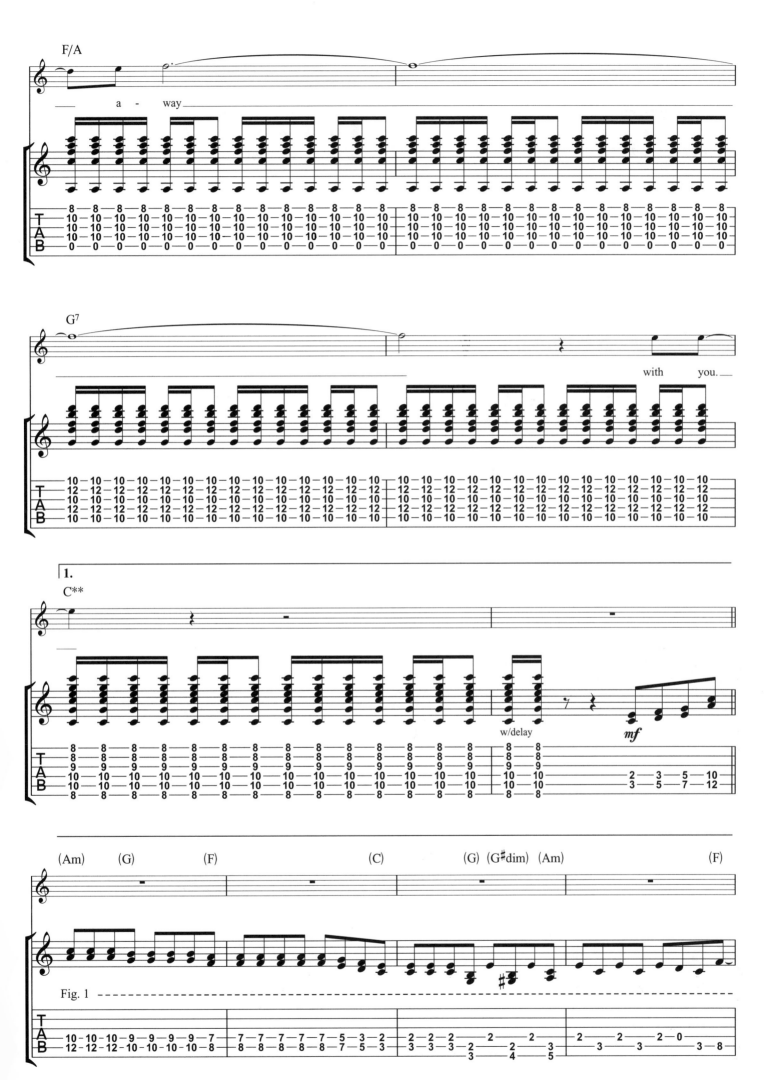

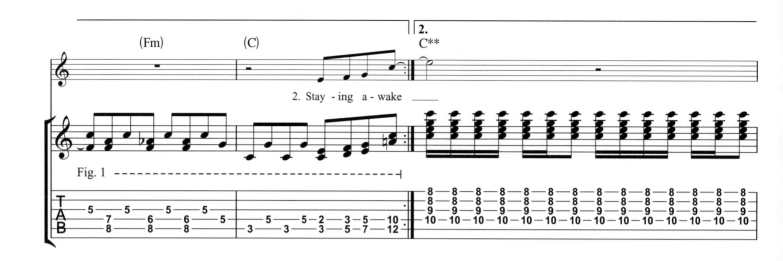

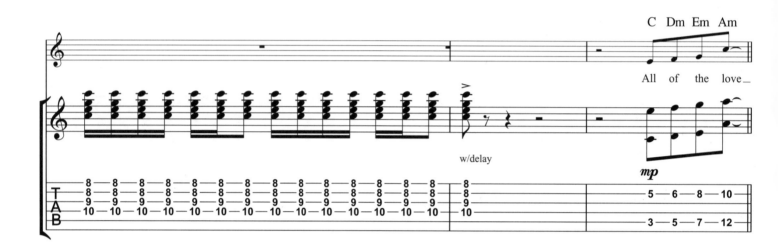

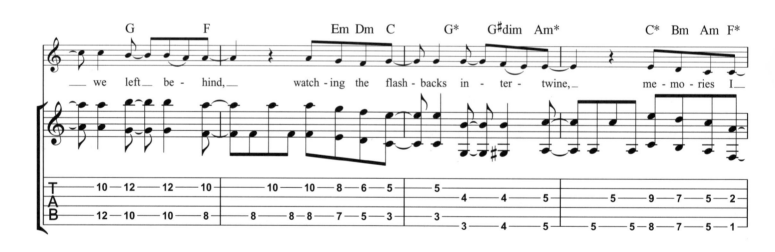

Interlude

Words by Matthew Bellamy
Music by Matthew Bellamy, Chris Wolstenholme & Dominic Howard

Hysteria

Words by Matthew Bellamy
Music by Matthew Bellamy, Chris Wolstenholme & Dominic Howard

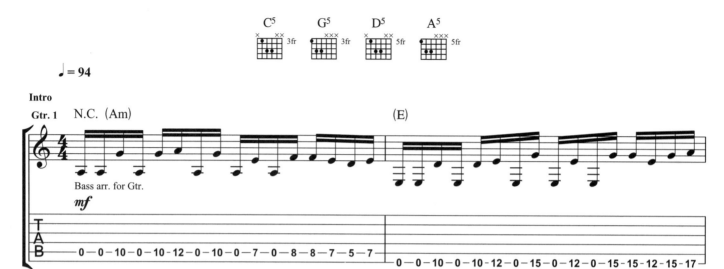

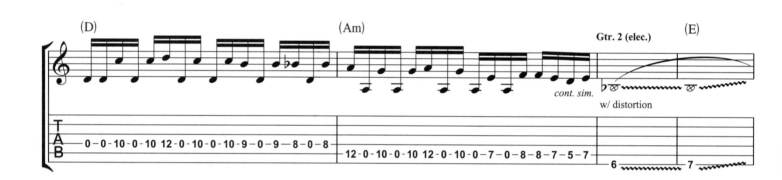

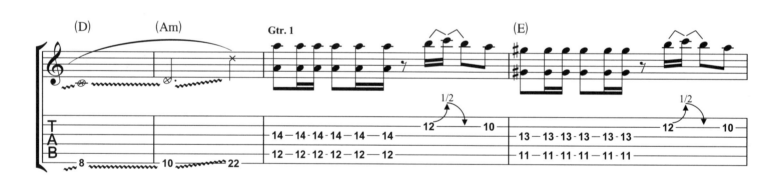

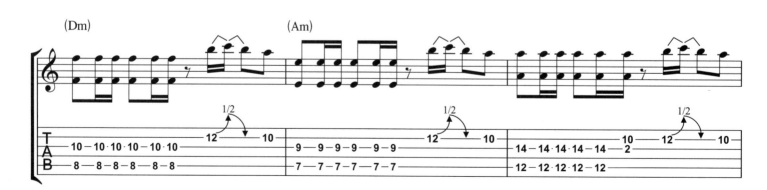

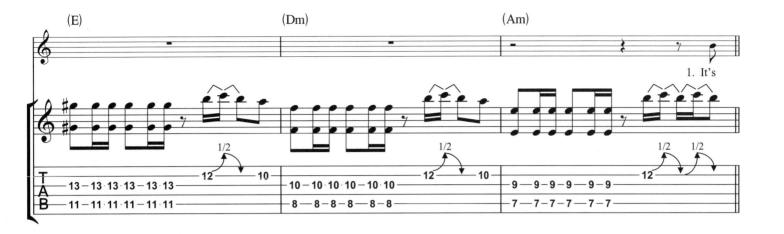

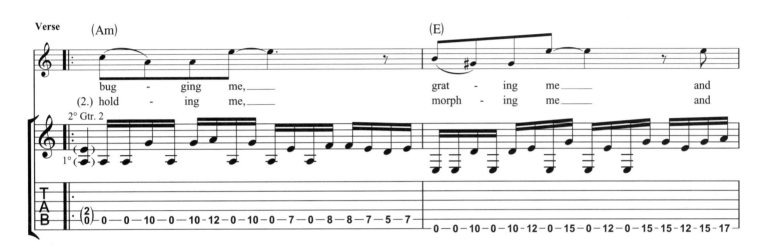

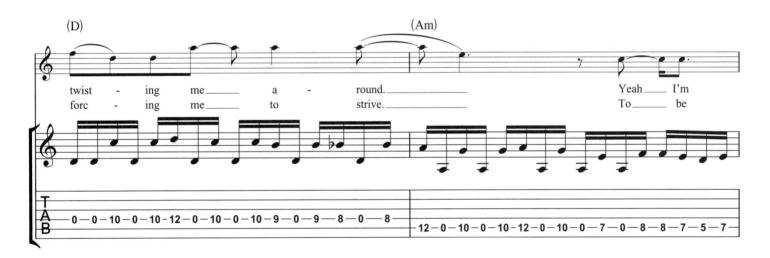

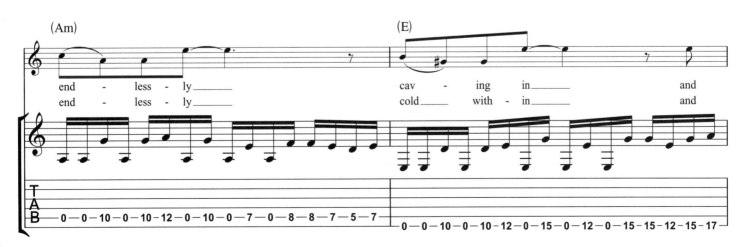

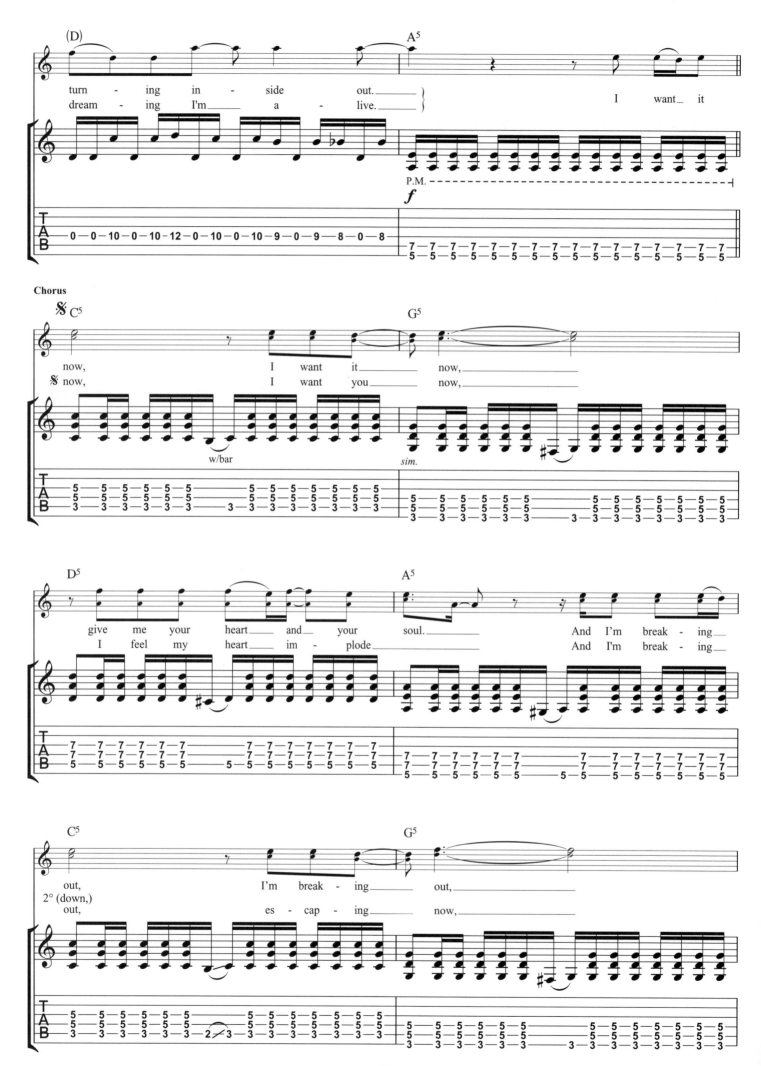

40

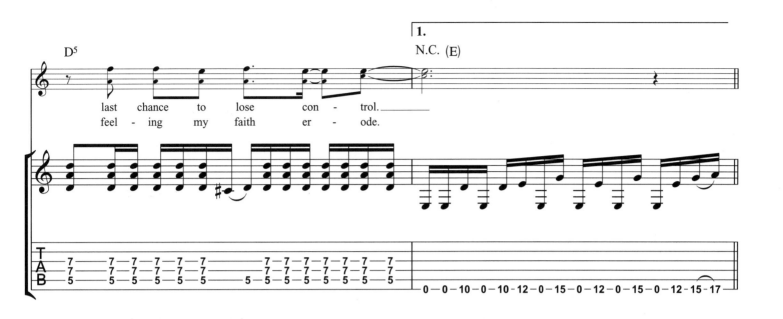

last chance to lose con - trol.

feel - ing my faith er - ode.

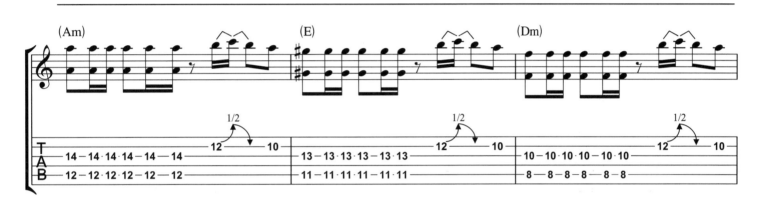

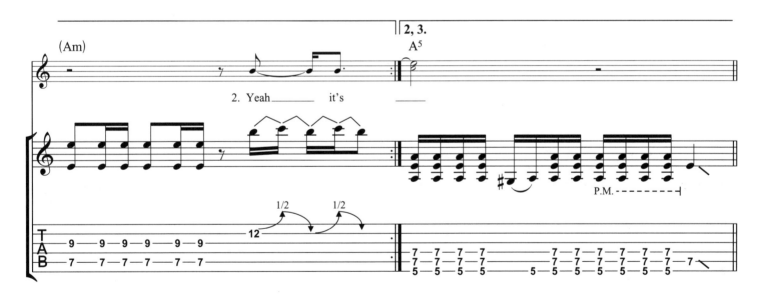

2. Yeah_____ it's

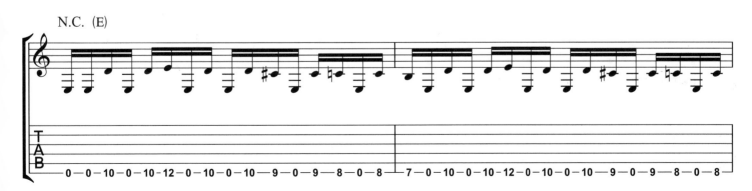

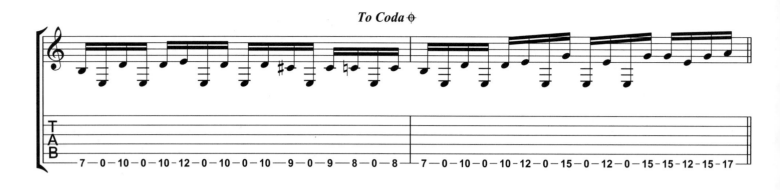

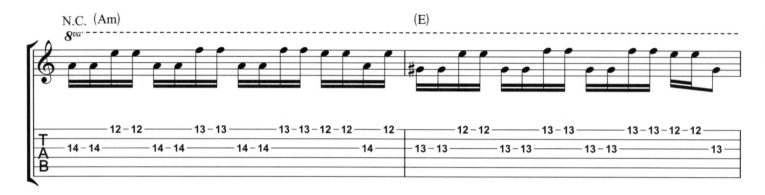

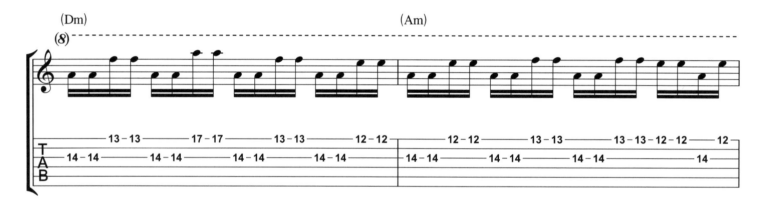

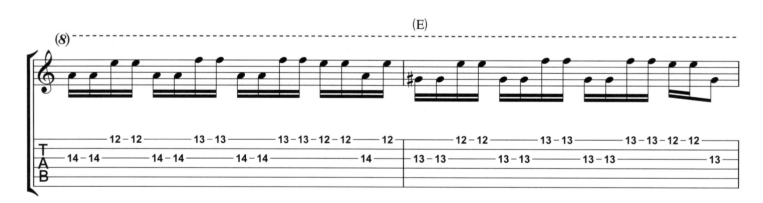

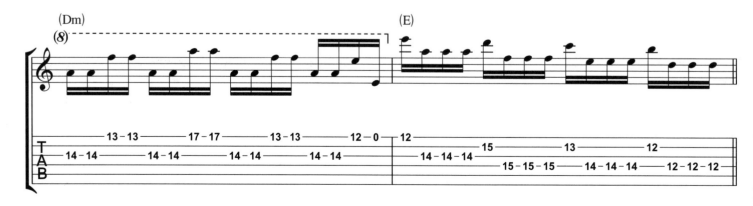

42

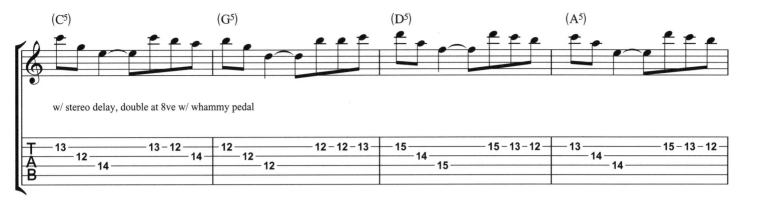

w/ stereo delay, double at 8ve w/ whammy pedal

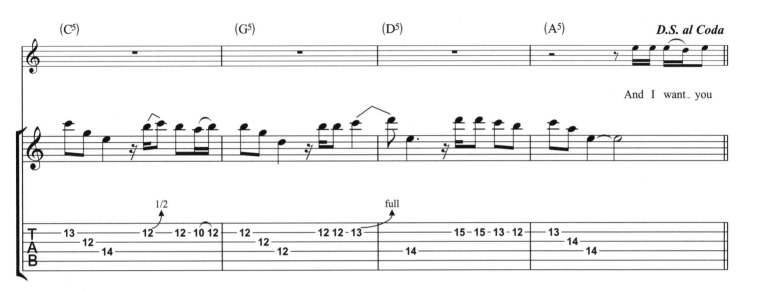

And I want_ you

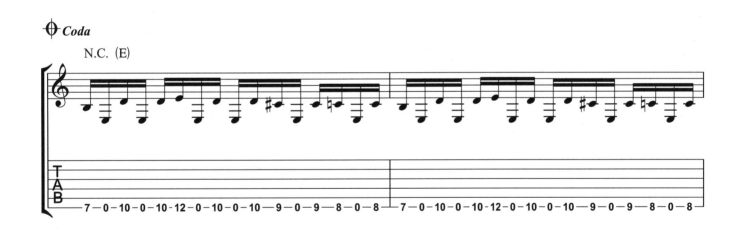

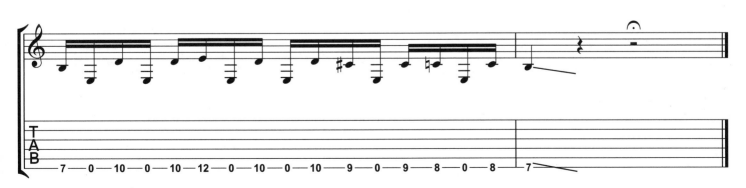

Blackout

Words by Matthew Bellamy
Music by Matthew Bellamy, Chris Wolstenholme & Dominic Howard

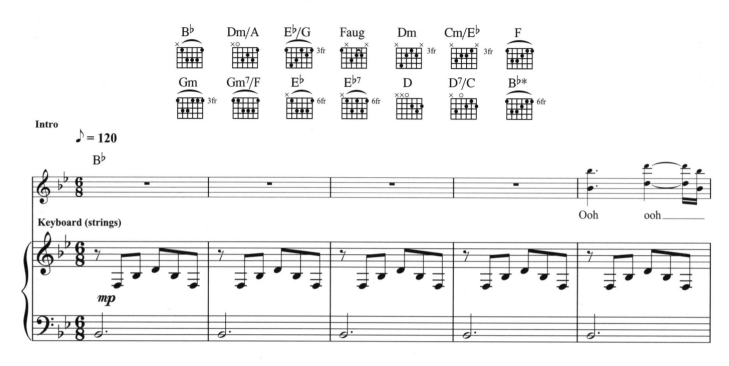

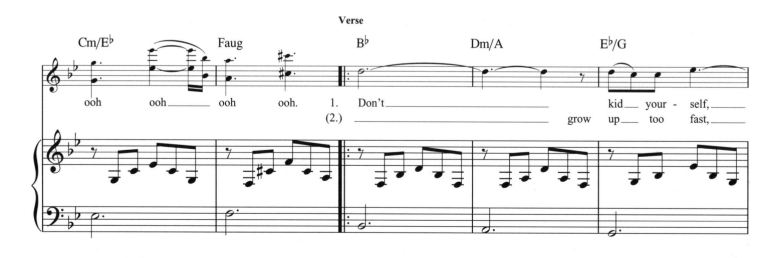

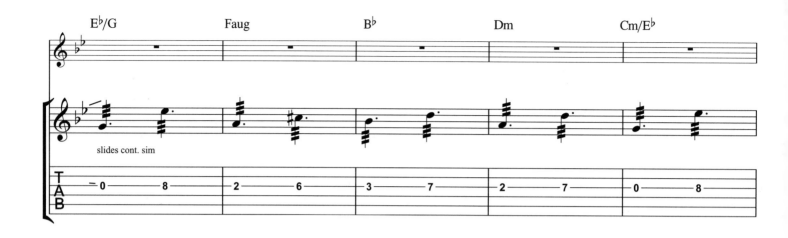

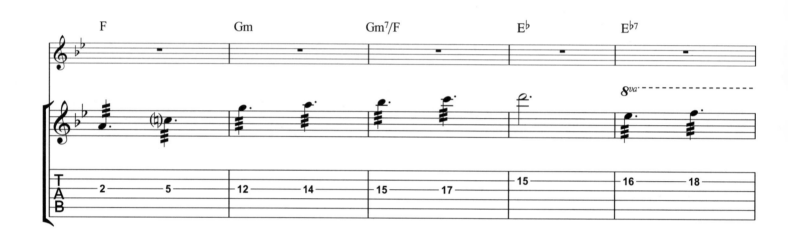

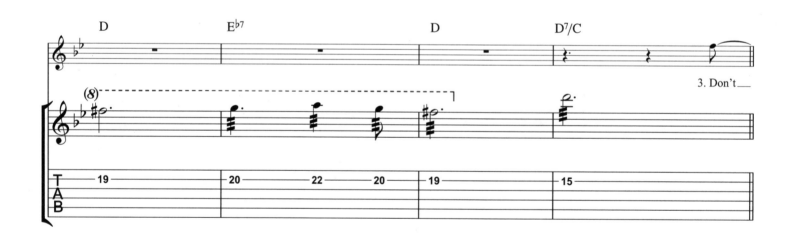

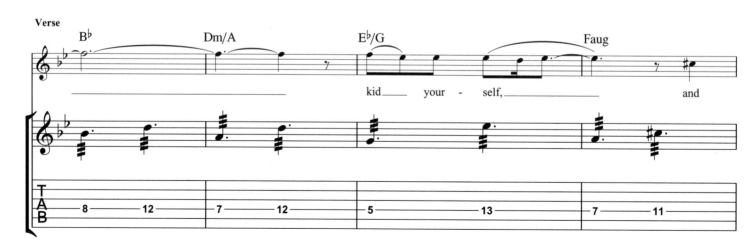

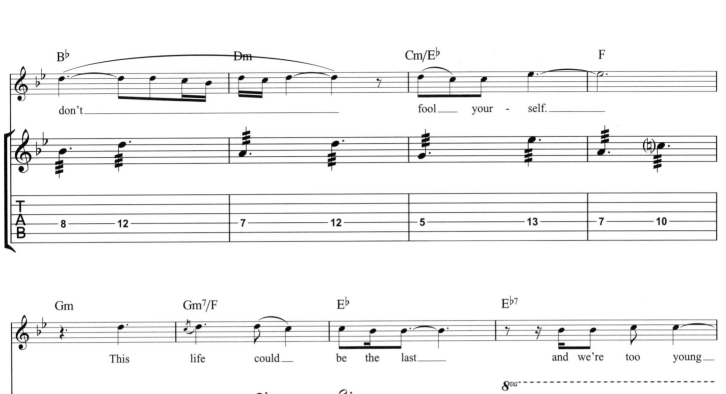

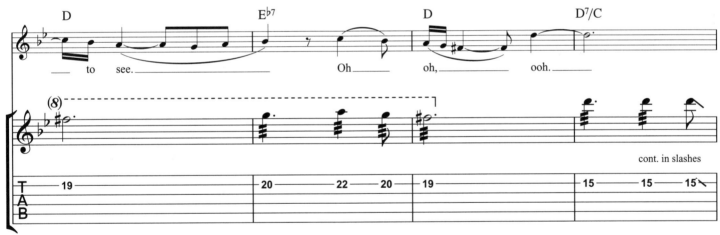

Butterflies & Hurricanes

Words by Matthew Bellamy
Music by Matthew Bellamy, Chris Wolstenholme & Dominic Howard

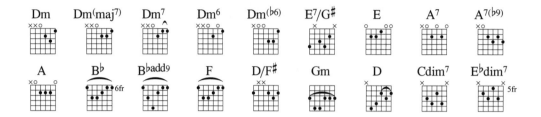

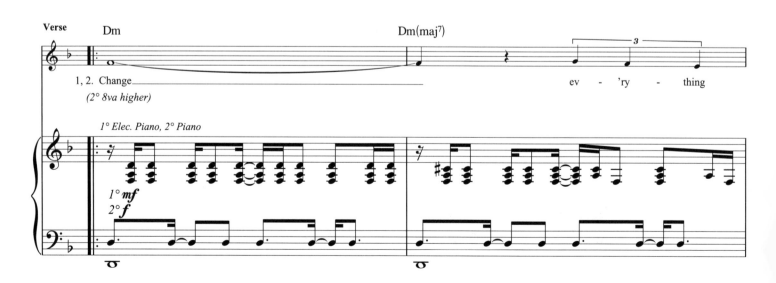

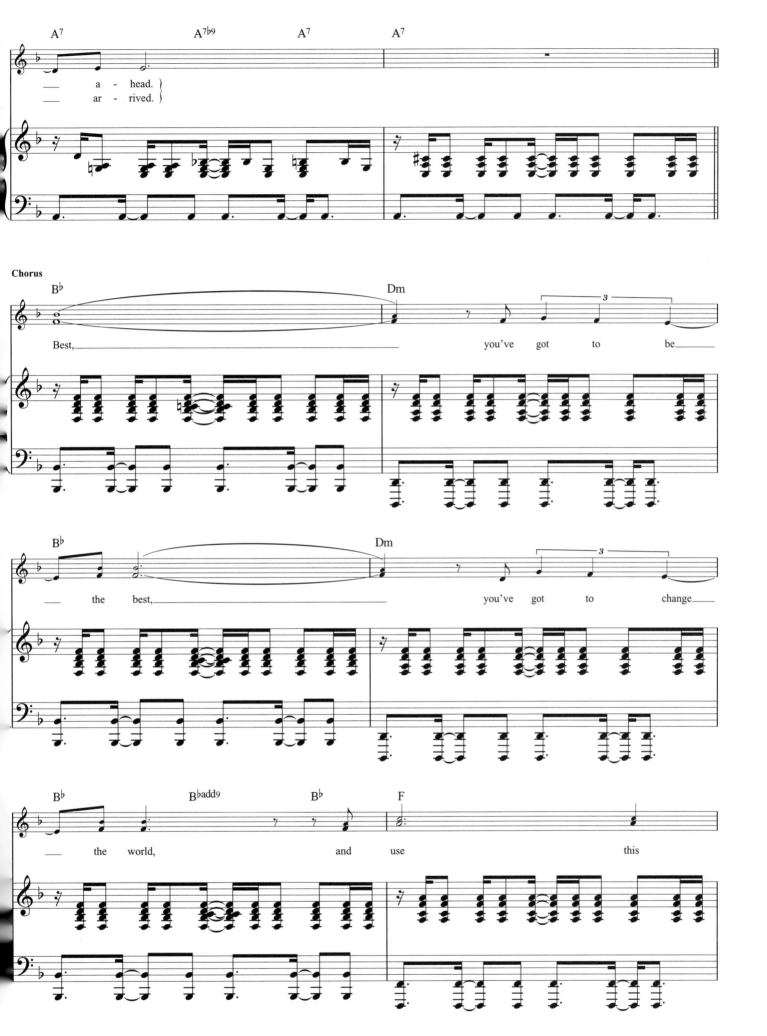

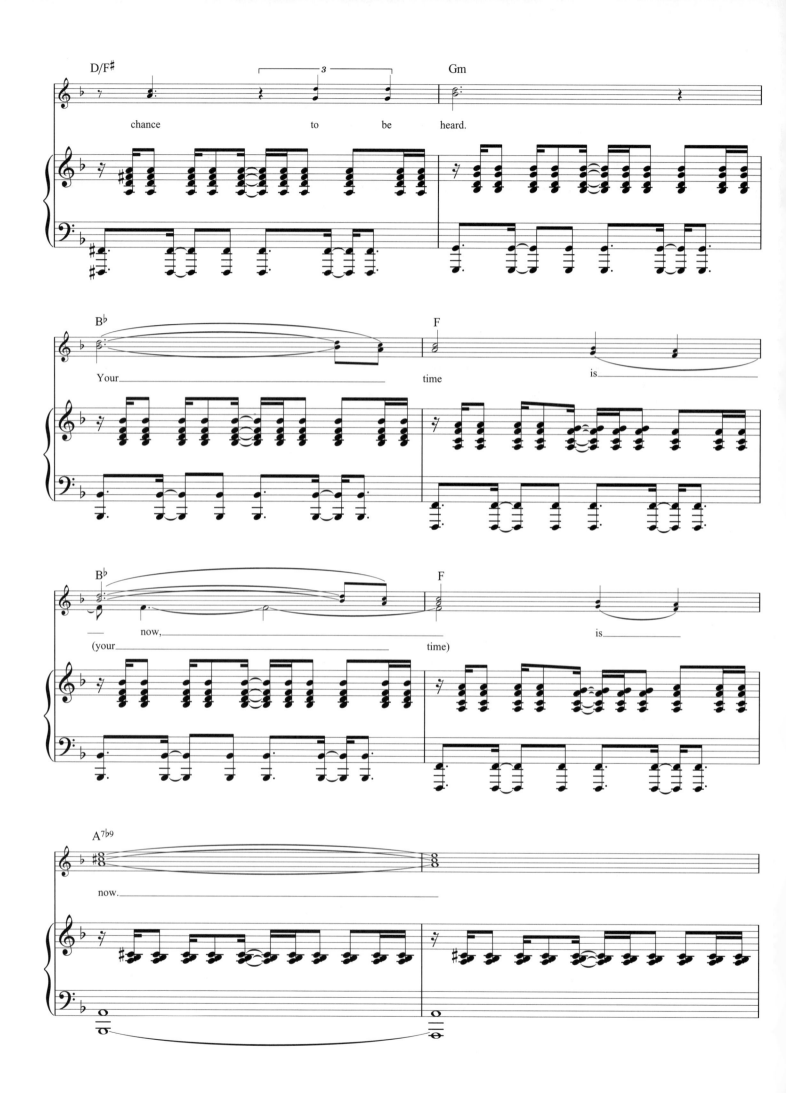

chance to be heard.

Your_____ time is_____

(your_____ now,_____ time) is_____

now._____

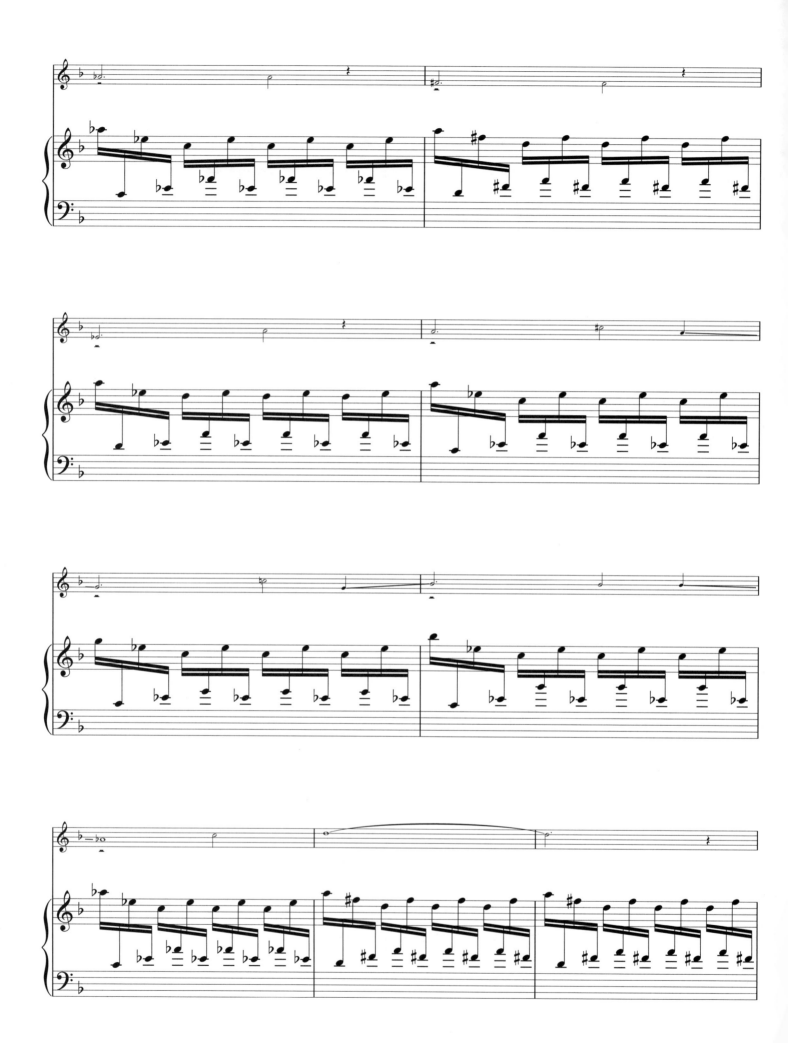

The Small Print

Words by Matthew Bellamy

Music by Matthew Bellamy, Chris Wolstenholme & Dominic Howard

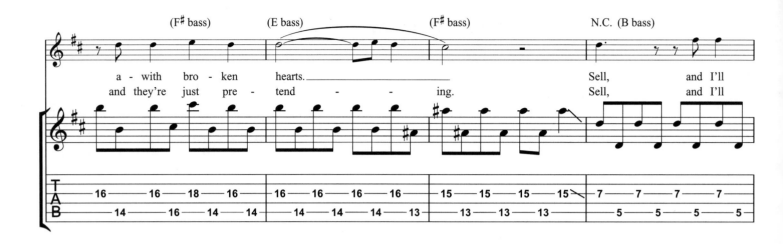

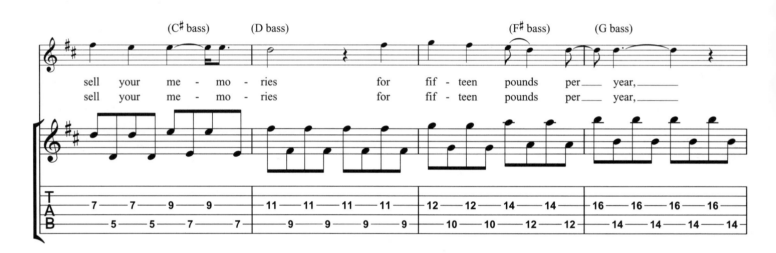

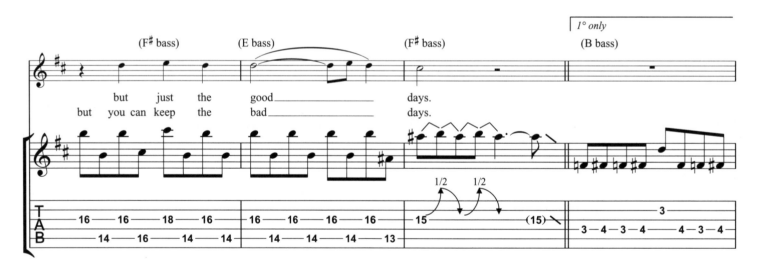

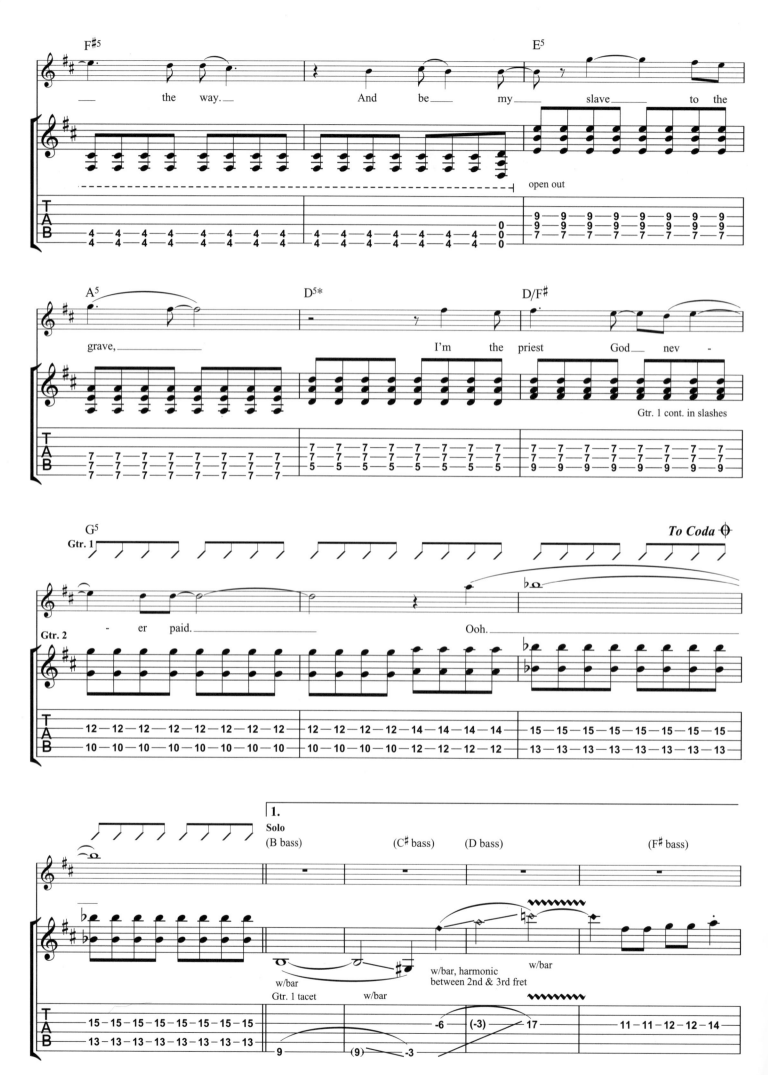

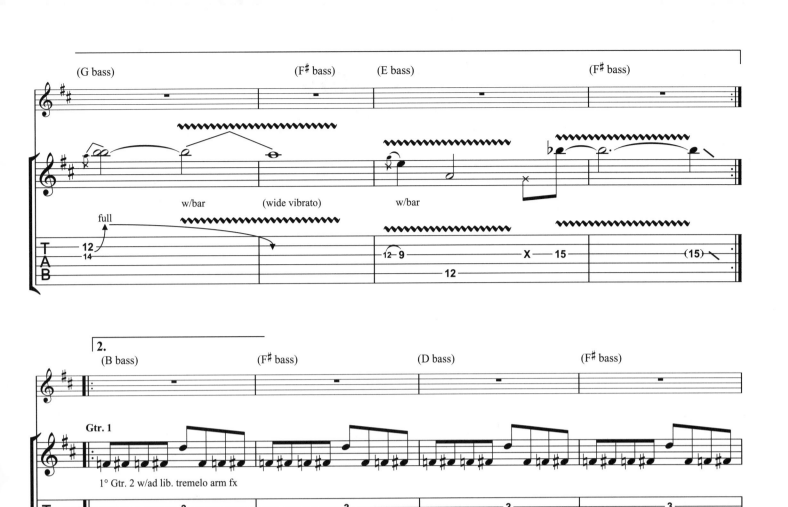

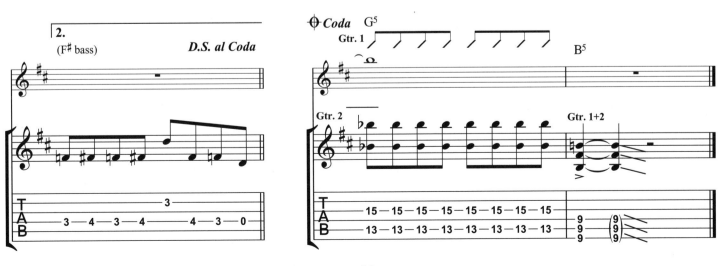

61

Endlessly

Words by Matthew Bellamy
Music by Matthew Bellamy, Chris Wolstenholme & Dominic Howard

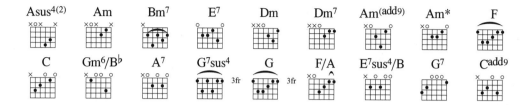

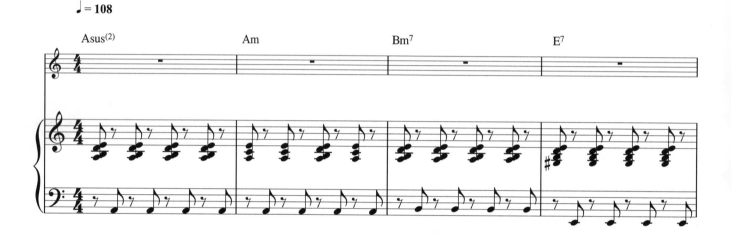

part_____ of me,____ you'll nev - er know.
plain_____ to see,____ it's try - ing_____ to speak.

Thoughts Of A Dying Atheist

Words by Matthew Bellamy
Music by Matthew Bellamy, Chris Wolstenholme & Dominic Howard

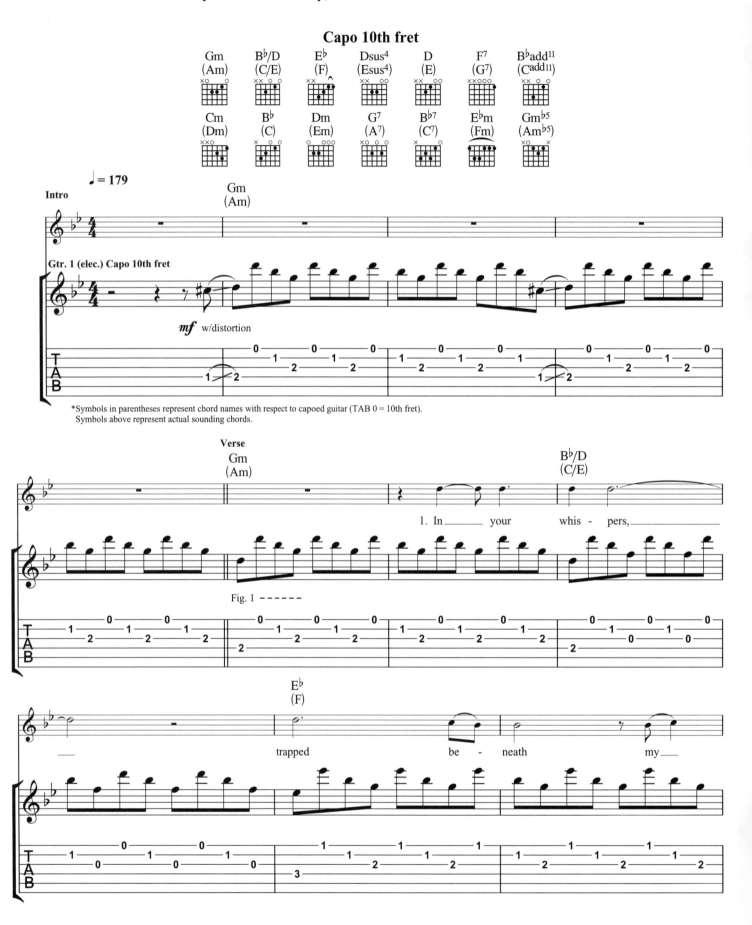

*Symbols in parentheses represent chord names with respect to capoed guitar (TAB 0 = 10th fret).
Symbols above represent actual sounding chords.

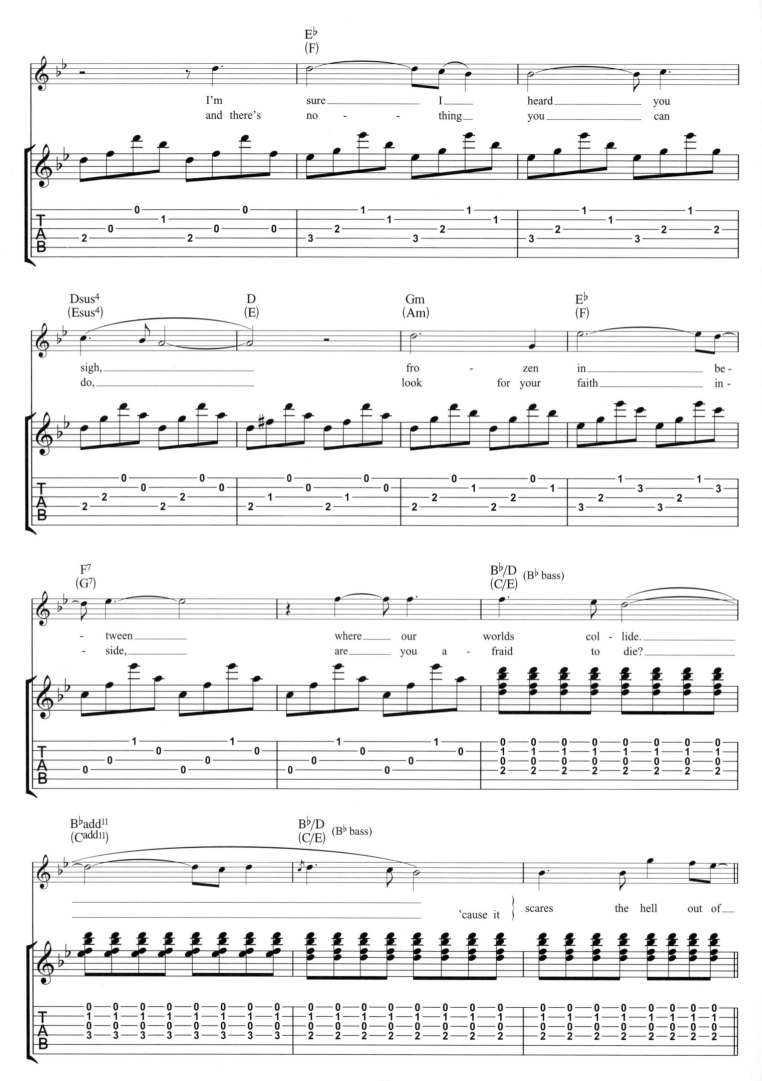

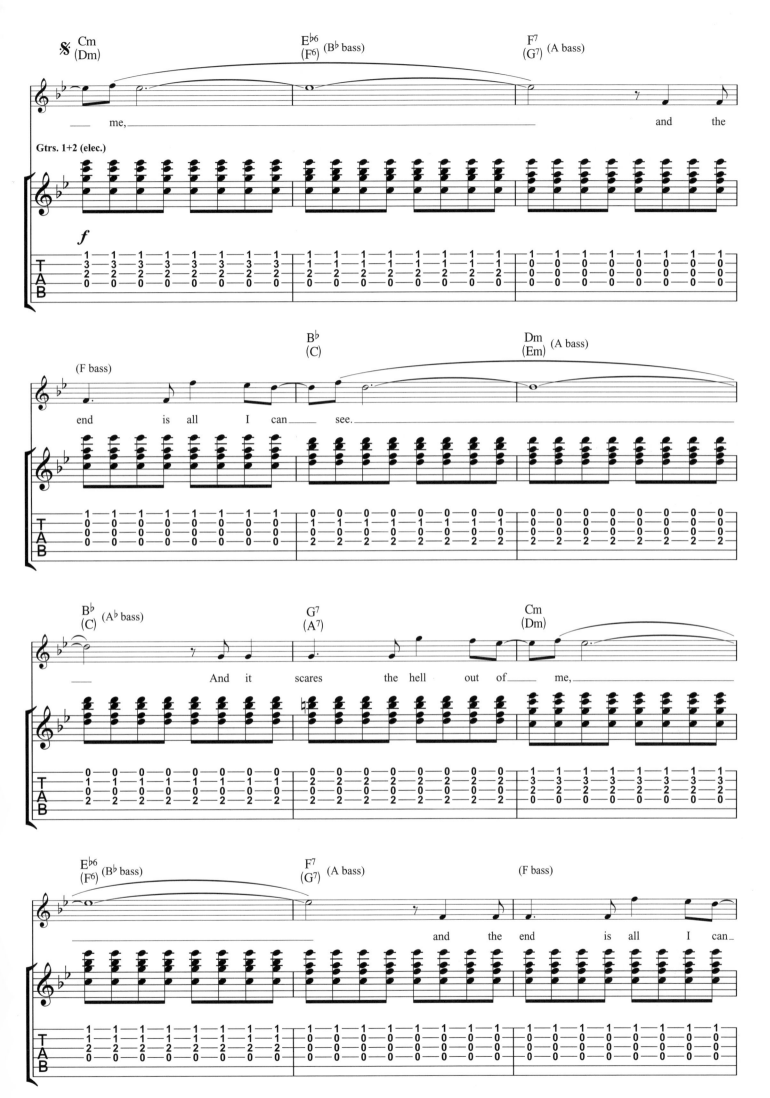

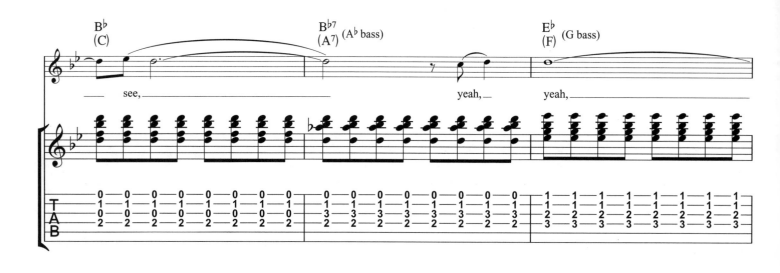

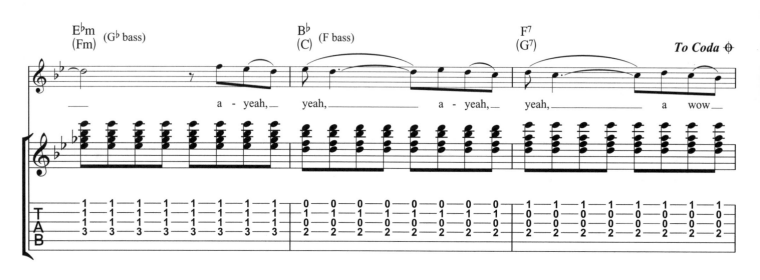

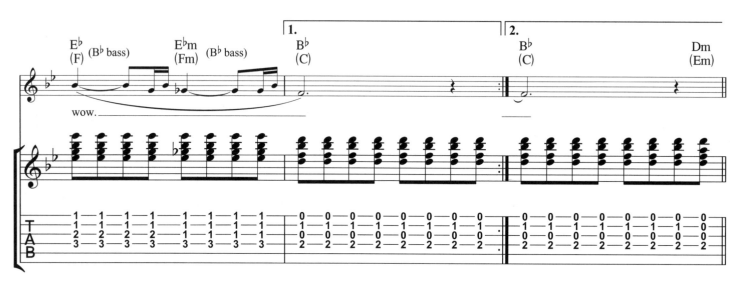

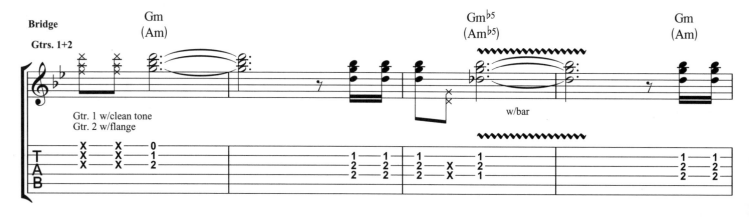

Ruled By Secrecy

Words by Matthew Bellamy
Music by Matthew Bellamy, Chris Wolstenholme & Dominic Howard

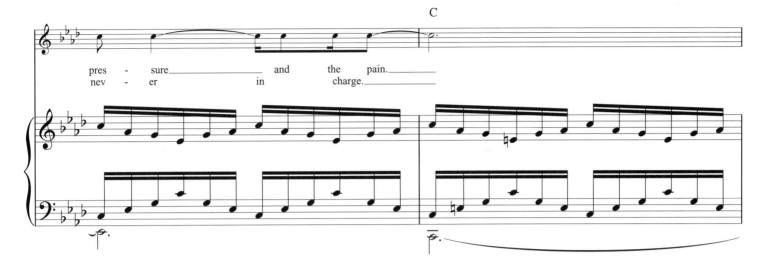

pres - sure_____ and the pain._____
nev - er in charge._____

Wash the blood off your hands,_____
Your death cre - ates_____

_____ suc - cess,_____ this time_____ she re -

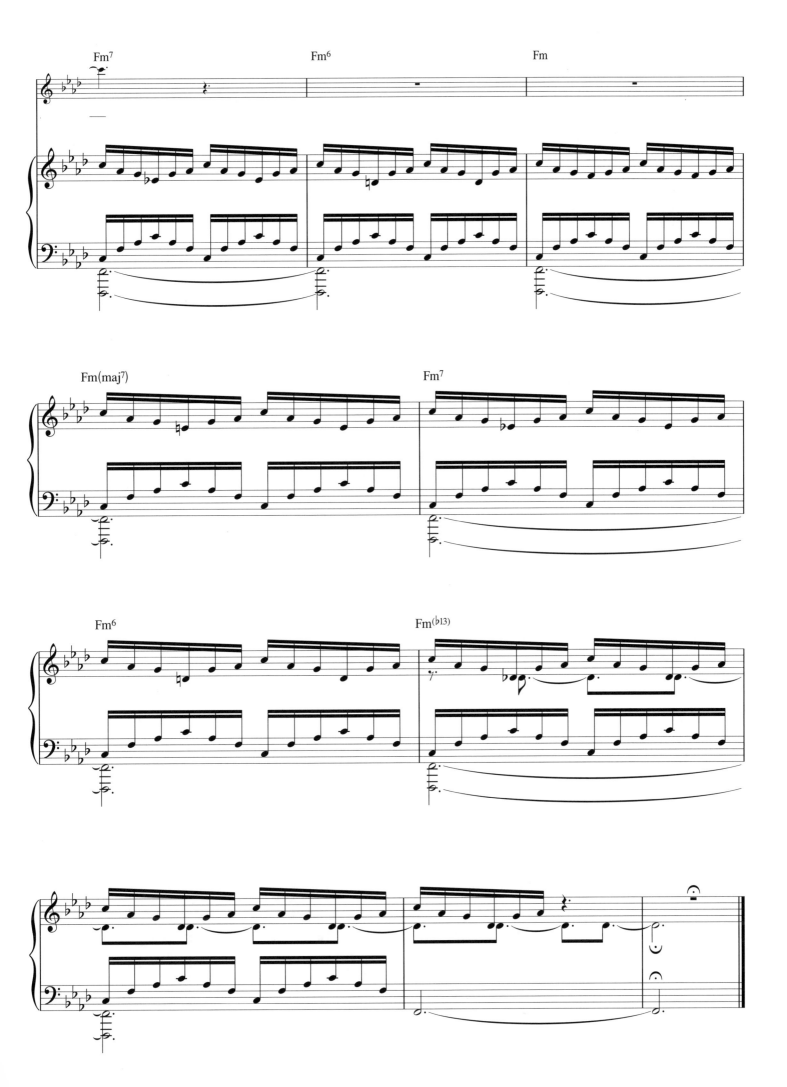

Guitar Tablature Explained

Guitar music can be notated in three different ways: on a musical stave, in tablature, and in rhythm slashes.

RHYTHM SLASHES are written above the stave. Strum chords in the rhythm indicated. Round noteheads indicate single notes.

THE MUSICAL STAVE shows pitches and rhythms and is divided by lines into bars. Pitches are named after the first seven letters of the alphabet.

TABLATURE graphically represents the guitar fingerboard. Each horizontal line represents a string, and each number represents a fret.

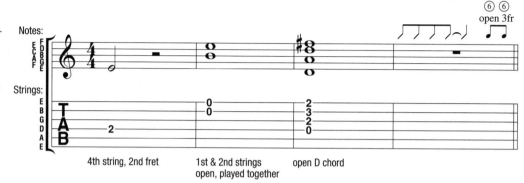

4th string, 2nd fret   1st & 2nd strings open, played together   open D chord

Definitions For Special Guitar Notation

SEMI-TONE BEND: Strike the note and bend up a semi-tone (1/2 step).

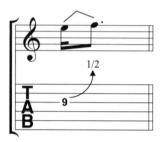

WHOLE-TONE BEND: Strike the note and bend up a whole-tone (whole step).

GRACE NOTE BEND: Strike the note and bend as indicated. Play the first note as quickly as possible.

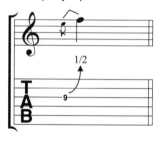

QUARTER-TONE BEND: Strike the note and bend up a 1/4 step.

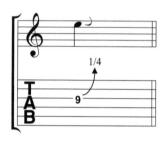

BEND & RELEASE: Strike the note and bend up as indicated, then release back to the original note.

COMPOUND BEND & RELEASE: Strike the note and bend up and down in the rhythm indicated.

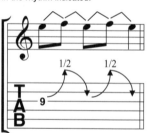

PRE-BEND: Bend the note as indicated, then strike it.

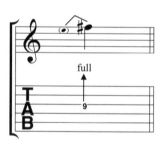

PRE-BEND & RELEASE: Bend the note as indicated. Strike it and release the note back to the original pitch.

UNISON BEND: Strike the two notes simultaneously and bend the lower note up to the pitch of the higher.

BEND & RESTRIKE: Strike the note and bend as indicated then restrike the string where the symbol occurs.

BEND, HOLD AND RELEASE: Same as bend and release but hold the bend for the duration of the tie.

BEND AND TAP: Bend the note as indicated and tap the higher fret while still holding the bend.

VIBRATO: The string is vibrated by rapidly bending and releasing the note with the fretting hand.

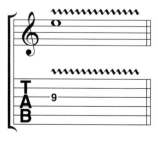

HAMMER-ON: Strike the first note with one finger, then sound the second note (on the same string) with another finger by fretting it without picking.

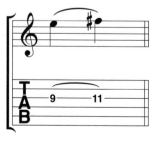

PULL-OFF: Place both fingers on the notes to be sounded, strike the first note and without picking, pull the finger off to sound the second note.

LEGATO SLIDE (GLISS): Strike the first note and then slide the same fret-hand finger up or down to the second note. The second note is not struck.

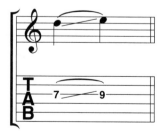

NOTE: The speed of any bend is indicated by the music notation and tempo.

SHIFT SLIDE (GLISS & RESTRIKE): Same as legato slide, except the second note is struck.

TRILL: Very rapidly alternate between the notes indicated by continuously hammering on and pulling off.

TAPPING: Hammer ("tap") the fret indicated with the pick-hand index or middle finger and pull off to the note fretted by the fret hand.

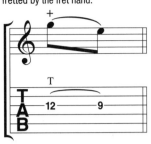

PICK SCRAPE: The edge of the pick is rubbed down (or up) the string, producing a scratchy sound.

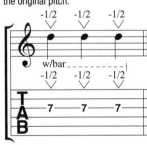

MUFFLED STRINGS: A percussive sound is produced by laying the fret hand across the string(s) without depressing, and striking them with the pick hand.

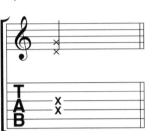

NATURAL HARMONIC: Strike the note while the fret-hand lightly touches the string directly over the fret indicated.

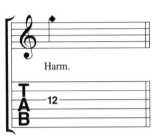

PINCH HARMONIC: The note is fretted normally and a harmonic is produced by adding the edge of the thumb or the tip of the index finger of the pick hand to the normal pick attack.

HARP HARMONIC: The note is fretted normally and a harmonic is produced by gently resting the pick hand's index finger directly above the indicated fret (in brackets) while plucking the appropriate string.

PALM MUTING: The note is partially muted by the pick hand lightly touching the string(s) just before the bridge.

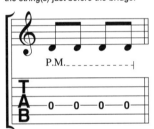

RAKE: Drag the pick across the strings indicated with a single motion.

TREMOLO PICKING: The note is picked as rapidly and continuously as possible.

ARPEGGIATE: Play the notes of the chord indicated by quickly rolling them from bottom to top.

SWEEP PICKING: Rhythmic downstroke and/or upstroke motion across the strings.

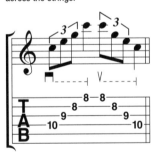

VIBRATO DIVE BAR AND RETURN: The pitch of the note or chord is dropped a specific number of steps (in rhythm) then returned to the original pitch.

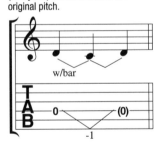

VIBRATO BAR SCOOP: Depress the bar just before striking the note, then quickly release the bar.

VIBRATO BAR DIP: Strike the note and then immediately drop a specific number of steps, then release back to the original pitch.

Additional Musical Definitions

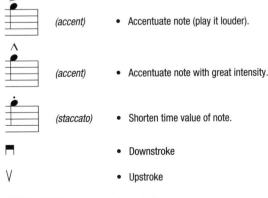

(accent)	•	Accentuate note (play it louder).
(accent)	•	Accentuate note with great intensity.
(staccato)	•	Shorten time value of note.
∏	•	Downstroke
V	•	Upstroke

NOTE: Tablature numbers in brackets mean:
1. The note is sustained, but a new articulation (such as hammer on or slide) begins.
2. A note may be fretted but not necessarily played.

D.%. al Coda

D.C. al Fine

tacet

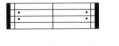

• Go back to the sign (%), then play until the bar marked *To Coda* ⊕ then skip to the section marked ⊕ *Coda*.

• Go back to the beginning of the song and play until the bar marked *Fine*.

• Instrument is silent (drops out).

• Repeat bars between signs.

• When a repeated section has different endings, play the first ending only the first time and the second ending only the second time.

10/04 (52729)

ca

rce... e captured
... presid...tial
on the ... of
...leaders — it

...ders of

...nd

...osed
the few
to have

...d, as growing
...end occupy-
...olence.
...a US ...ier
...nother wounded in
...ng at a ...trol station.
...meri... ...roops ha...
since 'combat ope...
on ... ... Yester-

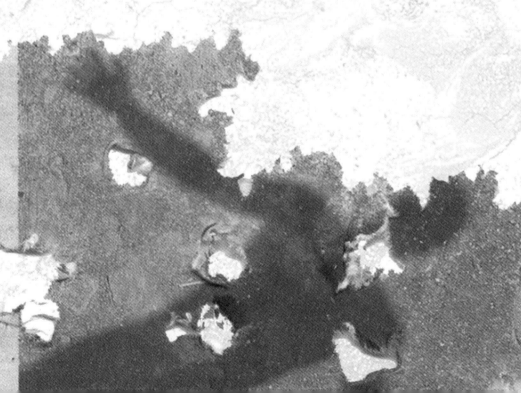